PHYSICS

BRAIN MAPPING ACADEMY

IIT

FOUNDATION & OLYMPIAD EXPLORER

CLASS
6

PRIME SERIES

BRAIN MAPPING
A C A D E M Y
Mapping Your Future

Published by:

Brain Mapping Academy

#16–11–16/1/B, First Floor,
Farhat Hospital Road,
Saleem Nagar, Malakpet,
Hyderabad–500 036
Telangana, India.
℗ 8142 635 635, 040-66135169
E–mail: info@bmatalent.com
Website: www.bmatalent.com

ISBN: 978-81-90687-71-3

Disclaimer

Every care has been taken by the compilers and
publishers to give correct, complete and updated information.
In case there is any omission, printing mistake or any
other error which might have crept in inadvertently,
neither the compiler / publisher nor any of the
distributors take any legal responsibility.

*In case of any dispute, all matters are subject to the exclusive
jurisdiction of the courts in Hyderabad only.*

First Edition: 2018

Preface

Today's learning culture demands high degree of efficiency from students, both in calculating and functioning, in order to excel. Speed and accuracy play an important role in climbing the competitive ladder. Students need to understand the basic requirements and be on their toes at all times to identify appropriate information sources and use them to their best advantage.

The preparation required for the tough competitive examinations is fundamentally different from that required for the qualifying ones, like board examinations. A student can emerge successful in a qualifying examination by scoring the bare minimum percentage of marks, whereas in a competitive one, he/she has to perform better than others to always score higher.

This book contains all types of questions that a student is required to tackle at the foundation level. The exercises are sequenced as Basic Practice and Further Practice, equipped with Single and/or Multiple Answer Questions, Paragraph Questions and Conceptual Questions in addition to other basic directing formats such as filling the gaps and true or false. Questions about direct application of concepts are covered under Basic Practice. More challenging questions about direct application are covered under Further Practice. Additionally, questions involving higher order of thinking or an open-ended approach, are covered under Brain Nurtures/Concept Drills.

This **IIT Foundation & Olympiad Explorer - Prime Series** is developed covering your **entire curriculum** and **added foundation topics**, providing you with a sturdy base, thorough understanding and detailed exposure to the subject, simultaneously equipping you well with a better understanding and control in overall application of the knowledge acquired, for the IIT entrance exam, setting you free to thrive and leap to the summit of success.

Suggestions and feedback from the teacher and student community are most welcome, as we consider it valuable in shaping a better ensuing edition.

Publisher

CONTENTS

Motion and Measurement

Synopsis

The process of comparing an unknown quantity with a known (standard) quantity of same kind is called **measurement**. In this process, a quantity that can be measured (i.e., physical quantity) needs to be identified. The measured physical quantities are expressed by following a certain system of units.

Ancient Methods of Measurement

The units used in olden days to measure length were foot length, arm/cubit length, i.e., the length from elbow to the tip of middle finger and length covered by a pace.

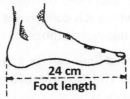

24 cm
Foot length

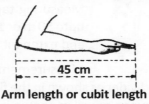

45 cm
Arm length or cubit length

Measurements made by using such units were NOT consistent because length of body parts of different persons are NOT the same. Hence, standard units are used for measurement. For uniformity and convenience, a basic set of units known as S.I. units have been accepted by scientists all over the world for measuring physical quantities like length, area, volume, etc. There are mainly three systems of units used for measuring physical quantities as shown in the table below.

Name of the Measuring system	Basic Units		
	Length	**Mass**	**Time**
MKS	Metre	Kilogram	Second
CGS	Centimetre	Gram	Second
FPS	Foot	Pound	Second

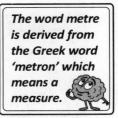

The word metre is derived from the Greek word 'metron' which means a measure.

Measurement in every day life: It is not always convenient to use basic SI units. To measure large or small quantities multiples or submultiples of basic units are frequently used.

Measurement of Length

Length is the distance between two fixed points. The SI unit of length is metre (m) and its C.G.S unit is centimetre (cm). The various units used to measure length are μm, mm, cm, m, km. The inter – relationship among these units with a standard unit can be given as

$1\ \mu m = 10^{-6}\,m$; $1\ mm = 10^{-3}\,m$; $1\ cm = 10^{-2}\,m$; $1\ km = 10^{3}\,m$;

$1\ Angstrom = 10^{-10}\,m$; $1\ fermi = 10^{-15}\,m$

Measurement of length of an object is done by various measuring devices like scale, metre scale, measuring tape etc. To measure the length of a wooden block, the zero mark on the scale is made to coincide with one end of the wooden block as shown. The reading on the other end of the wooden block gives its length.

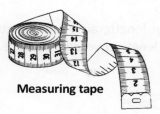
Measuring tape

Measuring tape is most commonly used by tailors to take measurements of length of body parts like chest, waist etc., that cannot be measured accurately by a scale.

Measuring tapes are also used for measuring longer lengths upto 50 m or 100 m where it is convenient to carry a rolled tape and extend it to the desired distance.

Measurement of curved lines can be done by using a piece of thread or by a divider as shown in the figure (1). The diameter of a uniform wire is found by winding it over a pencil as shown in the figure (2).

$$\text{Diameter of the wire} = \frac{\text{Distance spanned by the windings}}{\text{Number of turns}}$$

The diameter of a spherical object can be measured by placing the object between two wooden blocks as shown in the figure (3).

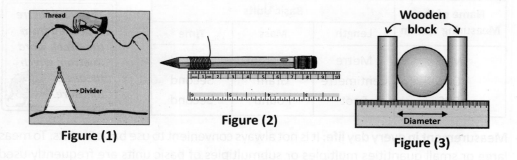

Figure (1)

Figure (2)

Figure (3)

➤➤➤ Measurement of very large distances

Distance between the earth and the moon, or the earth and the sun cannot be measured by using conventional units. Such large distances are expressed in the following units.

Astronomical Unit (au)

It is the average distance of the earth from the sun 1 au = 1.496×10^{11} m.

It is also used to express interplanetary distances.

Light year

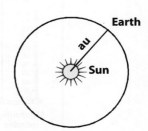

It is the distance travelled by light through vacuum in one year.

1 light year $= 365.25 \times 24 \times 3600 \, s \times 3 \times 10^8 \, m\, s^{-1}$

$\qquad\qquad = 9.46728 \times 10^{15} \, m$

This unit is used to measure distance between stars.

➤➤➤ Measurement of Height

Height is a vertical measurement of length. By using a measuring tape, we can make marks on the wall starting from the floor upto 7 metres. Height of students or persons can be measured by making them stand near the wall and placing a scale horizontally on their head coinciding with a reading. Their correct height can be expressed in centimetres and metres.

➤➤➤ Measurement of Area

Area is the amount of surface occupied by an object or a place. Area of a regular surface like a rectangle or a square can be calculated by knowing its length and breadth (or) length of its side. The SI unit of area is m^2 or square metre. The other units of area are mm^{2}, cm^2, m^2, km^2 etc.,

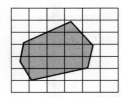

Larger areas are measured in 'acre' and 'hectare'. (1 acre = 4046.856 m^2, 1 hectare = 10000 m^2, 1 hectare = 2.471 acres) Area of an irregular surface is measured by using a graph paper as shown.

Area of one complete square is 1 unit and that of incomplete square is taken as half unit.

➤➤➤ Measurement of Volume

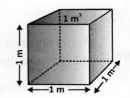

The space occupied by a substance (solid, liquid or gas) is called volume. The SI unit of volume is cubic metre. In short form cubic metre is written as m^3.

One cubic metre: It is the space occupied by a cube whose each side is equal to 1 m.

Volume of a regular shaped cuboid is given by volume = length × breadth × height

>>> **Measurement of volume of liquids**

To measure volume of liquids, certain devices used in our daily life are shown in figure (1).

The volume of irregular bodies can be measured by using **an over flow jar** as shown in figure (2).

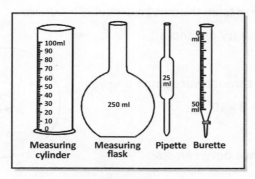
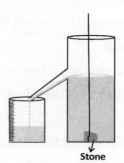

Figure - 1   **Figure - 2**

>>> **Measurement of Mass**

Mass is the amount of matter contained in a body. Mass is measured using devices like common balance, physical balance etc., SI unit of mass is kg. The other units of mass are milligram (mg), gram (g), quintal, tonne and so on...

Relationship between different units of mass	
1000 mg	= 1 g
1000 g	= 1 kg
100 kg	= 1 quintal
10 quintals	= 1 metric ton

>>> **Measurement of Time**

Time is the interval between two events. The SI unit of time is second. The different units of time are given below.

1 mean solar day	=	24 hours	1 minute	=	60 seconds
1 hour	=	60 minutes	1 year	=	365¼ days
1 decade	=	10 years	1 century	=	100 years
1 millennium	=	1000 years			

>>> **Motion**

Motion means movement. All living things move by themselves. Animals move from one place to another. They can move their body parts also.

Non–living things cannot move by themselves. They need force to move.

Ex: A stone has to be picked up. A vehicle has to be driven. Rain drops fall on the earth due to gravitational force.

⮞⮞⮞ Types of Motion

Linear (or) Translatory motion:

The motion in which all the particles of a body move through the same distance in the same time is called translatory motion.

There are two types of translatory motion:

(A) Rectilinear motion:

It is the motion of a body along a straight path.
It is also called linear translation.

Examples :

Movement of a toy car on the floor. A vehicle moving on a straight road. A ball dropped from a height.

(B) Curvilinear Motion:

It is the motion of a body along a curved path.
It is also called non-linear translation.

Examples :

A man walking on a crowded street from one end to the other end.

A bird diving into a lake to catch a fish and then flying up.

NOTE: Curvilinear and rectilinear motion are together referred as "TRANSLATORY MOTION".

Rotatory and Circular Motion:

Rotatory Motion	Circular Motion
1. Body remains in the same place with respect to time.	1. Body does not remain in the same place. It moves and changes position with time.
2. The body rotates about an axis passing through it.	2. It moves along a path whose axis may not pass through the body.
3. No linear motion is observed by the body as a whole. Examples: Merry-go-round, A potter's wheel, Blades of a mixer grinder	3. Body may undergo linear motion. Examples: Movement of the earth around the sun. Movement of a toy car along a circular road.

Periodic Motion

Motion which repeats at a regular intervals of time is called periodic motion.

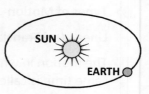

Examples :

i)   Motion of planets around the sun.

ii)   Motion of a simple pendulum. (It takes a fixed time to complete one oscillation).

iii) Motion of a piston of a motor car engine running at a constant speed.

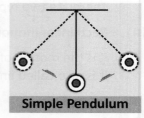

Simple Pendulum

Oscillatory Motion:

The to-and-fro or 'back and forth' motion of a body as a whole along the same path without change in shape is called oscillatory motion.

Examples :

A boy on a swing, motion of needle of a sewing machine, motion of simple pendulum

Vibratory Motion

It is another kind of oscillatory motion in which the body does not move as a whole but changes its shape.

Examples:

Motion of a stretched wire on sitar, or the prongs of a tuning fork.

NOTE: All oscillatory motions are periodic by nature but not vice versa.

Different Motions at the same time

Often a body exhibits different types of motion at the same time.

Eg: The Earth rotates about its axis while revolving around the sun.

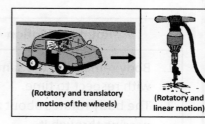

(Rotatory and translatory motion of the wheels)   (Rotatory and linear motion)

Distance

The length of the path taken by a moving body. The S.I. unit of distance is metre.

Speed

Speed of a body is the distance travelled in a unit time. S.I. unit of speed is m/s or m s⁻¹.

$$\text{Speed} = \frac{\text{Distance travelled}}{\text{Time}} \qquad \text{Average Speed} = \frac{\text{Total distance travelled}}{\text{Total time taken}}$$

Solved Examples

$\ggg$ **Example 1 :**

A 20 cm long string can go around a pencil 8 times. What is the circumference of the pencil ?

Solution:

Length of the string   = 20 cm

No. of turns around a pencil   = 8 times

Circumference of the pencil $= \dfrac{20}{8} = 2.5\,cm$

$\ggg$ **Example 2 :**

On a 120 km track, a train travels the first 30 km at a uniform speed of 45 km per hour. How fast must the train travel the next 90 km so as to average 60 km per hour for the entire trip ?

Solution:

Total distance travelled by the train = 30 + 90 = 120 km

Average speed = 60 km h^{-1}

Total time taken = $\dfrac{120}{60}$ = 2 h

Time taken for the first 30 km at a speed of 45 km h^{-1} = $\dfrac{30}{45} = \dfrac{2}{3}h$

Thus, the train has to cover the balance of 90 km in $2 - \dfrac{2}{3} = \dfrac{4}{3}h$

Hence, required speed will be $\dfrac{90 \times 3}{4} = 67.5\,kmh^{-1}$

$\ggg$ **Example 3 :**

A car travels at an average speed of 40 km h^{-1} for one hour and then at an average speed of 50 km h^{-1} for two hours. What is the total distance covered by the car ?

Solution:

>>>> **Example 4 :**

The water level in a measuring cylinder is 23 ml. When a stone was dropped into it, water rises to the mark of 58 ml. Find the volume of the stone.

Solution:

>>>> **Example 5 :**

A stone of volume 30 cm^3 is lowered into 60 cm^3 of water in a measuring cylinder as shown below. What will be the new reading in the measuring cylinder?

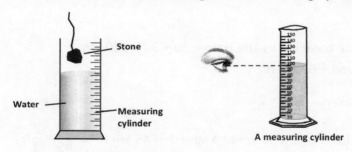

(A) 60 cm^3 (B) 30 cm^3 (C) 90 cm^3 (D) 100 cm^3

Solution : (C)

Initial reading = 60 cm^3

Volume of stone = 30 cm^3

∴ Final reading of measuring cylinder = 60 + 30 = 90 cm^3

>>>> **Example 6 :**

The thickness of a dozen coins on a metre scale was found to be 40 cm. What is the thickness of one coin ?

Solution :

Thickness of a dozen coins (12 coins)= 40 cm

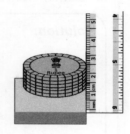

∴ Thickness of one coin = $\dfrac{40}{12}$ cm = $\dfrac{10}{3}$ cm = 3.33 cm

Concept Map

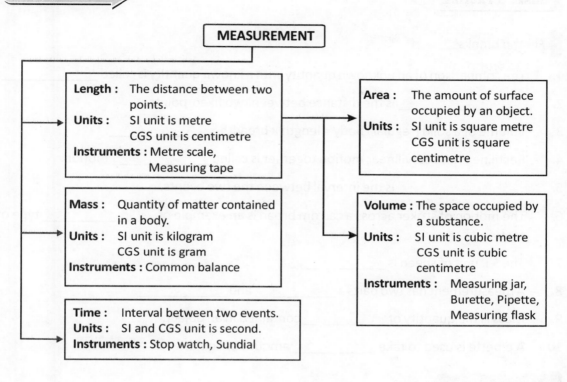

MEASUREMENT

Length : The distance between two points.
Units : SI unit is metre
CGS unit is centimetre
Instruments : Metre scale, Measuring tape

Area : The amount of surface occupied by an object.
Units : SI unit is square metre
CGS unit is square centimetre

Mass : Quantity of matter contained in a body.
Units : SI unit is kilogram
CGS unit is gram
Instruments : Common balance

Volume : The space occupied by a substance.
Units : SI unit is cubic metre
CGS unit is cubic centimetre
Instruments : Measuring jar, Burette, Pipette, Measuring flask

Time : Interval between two events.
Units : SI and CGS unit is second.
Instruments : Stop watch, Sundial

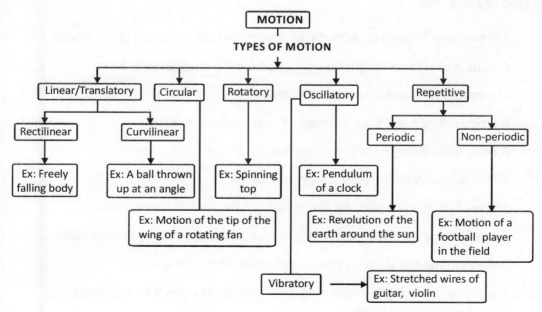

MOTION
TYPES OF MOTION

Linear/Translatory | Circular | Rotatory | Oscillatory | Repetitive

Rectilinear | Curvilinear

Periodic | Non-periodic

Ex: Freely falling body

Ex: A ball thrown up at an angle

Ex: Spinning top

Ex: Pendulum of a clock

Ex: Motion of the tip of the wing of a rotating fan

Ex: Revolution of the earth around the sun

Ex: Motion of a football player in the field

Vibratory → Ex: Stretched wires of guitar, violin

> **Basic Practice**

Fill the blanks

1. The comparison of an unknown quantity with a known quantity is called _____.

2. _____ is the distance between two fixed points.

3. Volume of a solid (regular) body = length × breadth × _____.

4. Rectilinear and curvilinear motion together is called _____ motion.

5. _____ is the interval between the two events.

6. The motion of striker across a carrom broad is an example of _____ type of motion.

7. The S.I. unit of speed is _____.

8. A measurement has two parts a _____ and _____.

9. Mass is the quantity of _____ contained in an object.

10. A pipette is used to take _____ amount of liquid.

True or False

1. The direction of motion of a body can be changed without application of any force.   (   )

2. A body is said to be in motion only if its position changes with time.   (   )

3. The motion of a spinning top is circular.   (   )

4. A freely falling body is an example of non–uniform motion.   (   )

5. A body undergoing circular motion may also have linear motion.   (   )

6. All periodic motions are oscillatory by nature.   (   )

7. Phases of moon is a periodic event that can be used to measure time.   (   )

8. Diameter of a spherical object cannot be measured by using a metre scale.   (   )

9. A standard unit is always a fixed measure of a physical quantity.   (   )

10. The choice of a length–measuring device depends upon the magnitude of measurement to be made.   (   )

Further Practice

▶▶▶ *Write the **correct option** as your answer on the line provided.*

1. **In increasing magnitude which of the following is correct ?** _____

    (A) m, cm, km, mm   (B) mm, cm, m, km

    (C) cm, mm, m, km   (D) mm, m, cm, km

2. **The motion of the arms of a soldier marching along the road is** _____

    (A) circular.   (B) oscillatory.   (C) rotatory.   (D) non-periodic.

3. **Which measurement is not expressed in correct S.I. unit ?** _____

    (A) 5 m of cloth   (B) 20 seconds of time

    (C) Surface area of 25 cm^2 (D) 2 kg cooking oil

4. **What is common in the motions shown below ?** _____

       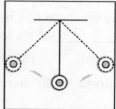

    (A) All motions are periodic   (B) All motions are oscillatory

    (C) All motions are rotational   (D) All motions are uniform

5. **The circumference of a basketball can be measured with a** _____

    (A) wooden ruler.   (B) measuring tape.

    (C) vernier calipers.   (D) measuring cylinder.

6. **One cubic metre is equal to** _____

    (A) 10^6 cc.   (B) 10^4 cc.   (C) 10^3 cc.   (D) 10^9 cc.

7. **1 litre =** _____

    (A) 10^{-2} m^3.   (B) 10^{-3} m^3.   (C) 10^{-4} m^3.   (D) 10^{-6} m^3.

8. **The space inside a container is known as its** _____

    (A) bottom.   (B) volume.   (C) capacity.   (D) area.

9. **Which one is not a unit for measuring time ?** _____

    (A) Hour   (B) Mean solar day

    (C) Minute   (D) Sundial

10. The passengers sitting in a flying aeroplane are in _____ with respect to clouds, but are at _____ with respect to the interior of the aeroplane. _____

(A) rest, motion

(B) rest, rest

(C) motion, rest

(D) motion, motion

11. The smallest time measured by a wrist watch accurately is _____

(A) 1 milli second.

(B) 60 seconds.

(C) 1 second.

(D) 1 hour.

12. Which of the following relations is correct about the speed of an object ? _____

(A) Speed = Distance × Time

(B) Speed = $\dfrac{\text{Distance}}{\text{Time}}$

(C) Speed = $\dfrac{\text{Time}}{\text{Distance}}$

(D) Speed = $\dfrac{1}{\text{Distance} \times \text{Time}}$

13. A boy wants to buy new shoes. To find out his correct shoe size, the _____ of his feet should be measured. _____

(A) length.   (B) thickness.   (C) area.   (D) volume.

14. The prefix "milli" used as a submultiple for metre is _____

(A) $\dfrac{1}{10}$.   (B) $\dfrac{1}{100}$.   (C) $\dfrac{1}{1000}$.   (D) 1000.

15. The motion of the pulley shown below is _____

(A) rotational.

(B) translational.

(C) circular.

(D) rectilinear.

16. The motion of the weight in the above activity is _____

(A) rotational.

(B) vibratory.

(C) circular.

(D) rectilinear.

17. Which part of the moving cycle shown below undergoes rotatory motion ? _____

(A) P

(B) Q

(C) R

(D) All of the above

18.　**The amount of surface of an object is called its**　　　　　＿＿＿＿＿＿

　　(A) volume.　　　(B) area.　　　(C) length.　　　(D) none of these.

19.　**The motion of the seconds hand of a clock is**　　　　　＿＿＿＿＿＿

　　(A) circular.　　　(B) rotatory.　　　(C) translatory.　　(D) curvilinear.

20.　**The appropriate unit for measuring thickness of a coin is**　　　＿＿＿＿＿＿

　　(A) centimetre.　(B) kilometre.　　(C) millimetre.　　(D) micrometre.

21.　**The level of water in a cylinder is 12.5 ml. When a stone is lowered in it, the level of water becomes 21.0 ml. What is the volume of the stone ?**　　＿＿＿＿＿＿

　　(A) 7.5 ml　　　(B) 33.5 ml　　　(C) 3.35 ml　　　(D) 8.5 ml

22.　**A man runs 10 km in 30 min. What is his average speed ?**　　＿＿＿＿＿＿

　　(A) 5 km h^{-1}　　(B) 20 km h^{-1}　　(C) 15 km h^{-1}　　(D) 20 km

》》》 *Write the **correct options** as your answer on the line provided.*

1.　**The motion of the wheels of a horse driven cart is**　　　　＿＿＿＿＿＿

　　(A) vibratory.　　(B) translatory.　(C) rotatory.　　(D) circular and translatory.

2.　**With regards to type of motion, which of the following statements is true ?**　　＿＿＿＿＿＿

　　(A) Swinging of arms of a soldier while marching is oscillatory.

　　(B) The beating of our heart and expansion/contraction of lungs are periodic.

　　(C) Motion of a spinning top is circular motion.

　　(D) A freely falling body undergoes rectilinear motion.

3.　**Which of the following statements is/are incorrect ?**　　　　＿＿＿＿＿＿

　　(A) Arm length or a footstep was used as a unit of length in olden days.

　　(B) The needle of a sewing machine undergoes circular motion.

　　(C) Motion of a body thrown upward at an angle is rectilinear motion.

　　(D) Multiples and submultiples of a unit are used for measurement of bigger or smaller quantities.

4.　**Nagender is playing soccer. The motion exhibited by the ball is/are**　　＿＿＿＿＿＿

　　(A) curvilinear.　(B) circular.　　(C) oscillatory.　　(D) non-uniform.

5.　**Which of the following is/are in periodic motion ?**　　　　＿＿＿＿＿＿

　　(A) A freely falling body　　　(B) A swinging pendulum

　　(C) Rotation of the earth　　　(D) A flying kite

6. **When a drill bores a hole in a piece of wood, the type of motion is** _____

   (A) rotatory.   (B) translatory.

   (C) curvilinear.   (D) none.

7. **Which of the following is/are not in translatory motion ?** _____

   (A) A ball delivered by a spin bowler

   (B) A drill that bores a piece of wood

   (C) A spinning wheel

   (D) Moving rear wheel of a bicycle on its stand

8. **Which one undergoes periodic motion ?** _____

   (A) Rotation of the earth.

   (B) Motion of seconds hand of a clock.

   (C) A spinning top.

   (D) Heart beat of a resting normal person.

9. **Identify an example of oscillatory motion.** _____

   (A) The motion of prongs in a tuning fork.

   (B) A child on a swing.

   (C) The motion of a pendulum.

   (D) Motion of a car on a straight road.

10. **Which of the following cannot change their position ?** _____

    (A) A tree   (B) A building

    (C) An aeroplane   (D) A mountain

> **Numerical Problems**

1. A plastic box measures 20 cm × 30 cm × 40 cm. If a container of 240 cm³ in volume is used to take water to fill up the box, how many times must the container be used ?

2. A bus leaves place A at 8.30 AM. It reaches place 'B' located at a distance of 80 km at 10.30 AM. It makes a scheduled halt of 30 minutes and then starts for place 'C' which is 60 km from B. If it reaches 'C' at 1 pm. Find the average speed of the bus.

3. A helicopter takes 5 minutes to travel from terminal X to terminal Y. If the distance between terminals X and Y is 2000 m, what is the average speed of the helicopter ?

4. A car has to cover 250 km in 5 hours. It covers the first 100 km in 3 hours. At what average speed, the car has to be driven so as to cover the balance distance within the scheduled time ?

5. Bhavana goes to school by taking straight line paths via AB, BC, CD as shown in the figure. Find the total distance travelled.

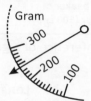

6. A bus starts from place 'A' with a speed of 90 km h^{-1}. Another bus starts at the same time at a speed of 20 m s^{-1}. Which of the two buses is faster ?

7. With what speed should a car travel so that it can cover a distance of 5 km in 10 minutes?

8. Rajesh takes 20 minutes to reach his school with a speed of 5 m s^{-1}. How far is his school ?

9. Find the place value of decades, century, millennium in 2009 year.

10. A scooter weighs 0.22 tonnes. Express it in kg .

11. An express train travelling at 30 m/s takes 3 seconds to pass a station. What is the length of the train ?

12. What is the reading on the scale shown below ?

13. While measuring the diameter of a ball, a student noted that the inner edges of the wooden blocks is between 3.4 cm and 4.7 cm on a scale. Calculate the diameter of the ball.

14. Calculate the mass of water in a tank of length 40 cm, breadth 30 cm and height 10 cm, if mass of 1 cm^3 of water is 1 g.

15. How many seconds are equivalent to 5 h 25 min ?

16. The height of Ram is 50 cm more than Harish. If the combined height of both Ram and Harish is 2.8 m. What are their heights?

17. Express 5 m^3 in terms of millilitre.

18. Rajesh takes 15 s to walk 100 m. How much time will he take to cover 5 km?

19. A measuring cylinder has 125 cm^3 of water. When 2 pebbles are dropped into the cylinder, the water level rises to 150 cm^3. What is the volume of each pebble?

20. The length and breadth of a rectangular floor of a room are 5metres and 4 metres respectively. Calculate the area of the floor.

21. A car travels at a speed of 30 km per hour for 30 minutes and then at a speed of 45 km per hour. What is the total distance travelled by the car in 2 hours?

22. A car takes 4 hours to travel from one city to another and the distance between the two cities is 260 km. Find the speed of the car.

23. The thickness of 50 turns of a wire on the scale was found to be 64 cm. What is the thickness of the wire?

Conceptual Questions

1. What is the difference between area and volume ?

2. What kind of motion does a satellite undergo around a planet ?

3. How are days and nights caused ?

4. What kind of motion is the free fall of an apple from a tree ?

5. John is given the following items and he is asked to find the volume of only one marble. Explain how he can do it ?

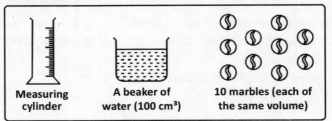

| Measuring cylinder | A beaker of water (100 cm³) | 10 marbles (each of the same volume) |

6. How will you measure the circumference of a given cylinder?

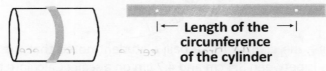

A paper strip wrapped around the cylinder

7. How will you measure the volume of a stone by using an overflow can ?

8. When does a change in shape and size of an object takes place ?

9. What kind of motion does a plastic ruler undergo when it is placed in between the brick and the table top as shown in figure (1) below ?

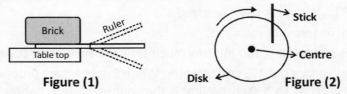

Figure (1)   **Figure (2)**

10. A circular disk with a stick is moving about its axis through the centre as shown in figure (2) above. What type of motion is exhibited by the stick ?

Brain Nurtures

1. What is the new name of litre ?

2. What is 'shake' ?

3. Two cars A and B are moving on a circular track in opposite direction. 'A' is moving at a constant speed of 2 m s⁻¹. What will be the speed of 'B' so that, it does not collide with 'A' ?

4. Which is the most accurate clock ?

5. What is the difference in the lengths of a mean solar day and a sidereal day ?

6. Tony was asked to read Tolstoy's War and Peace'. How many hours would he take to finish the book, given that he reads 1800 words in 10 minutes, and that there are 5000 words per page in the 456-page book ?

7. What is the possible volume of a full grown man ?

8. Two cyclists are moving towards each other with a speed of 4m/s each. Initially, they were 800 meters away. A naughty butterfly flies from the front of the wheel of one bicycle (point P) to the front of the wheel of the other (point Q), back and forth. If the speed of the butterfly is 6 m/s. Find the total distance that it travels before it is wedged in between.

Application Based

1. Fill the empty spaces in the given table.

	Time	Distance	Speed		Time	Distance	Speed		Time	Distance	Speed
(a)	5 s	100 m		(b)	10 s		6 m/s	(c)		48 m	12 m/s

2. How would you measure the volume of the following ?

   (a) Teaspoon of salt.   (b) Drop of glycerine.   (c) Piece of granite.

3. Why do we go for an atomic standard for defining 'metre' and 'second' ?

4. You have learned about several methods of keeping time such as measuring the length of a shadow (used in sundial), tracking the position of the moon (to keep track of months) etc. Golu devised a new method of keeping time where he wants to predict the time of the day depending on temperature of the surroundings. He made the following observations on one day.

Temperature	20° C	22° C	25° C	26° C	22° C
Time	6 AM	9 AM	12 Noon	3 PM	6 PM

He intends to use this data to estimate time the next few days.

   a) Is Golu's method of keeping time reliable ? Why/why not ?

   b) At some time the next day, Golu observed the temperature to be 21°C. Can he predict the time exactly using the data from the observations he made the previous day ?

   c) If temperature at sometime during the next day was found to be 26°C, what should be the time, according to Golu's method ?

   d) Is the time estimated according to Golu's method in the previous question necessarily correct ?

2

Light, Shadows and Reflections

Synopsis

》》 Light

One of the forms of energy is light. When this energy falls on the objects, it bounces back from the surface of objects and enters our eyes. Thus, light is an invisible form of energy that causes in us sensation of sight (vision) and enables us to see objects.

》》 Sources of Light

Sun is one of the important sources of light. In addition to this a burning candle, a lighted torch, a glowing tube light, kerosene oil lamp etc., are also other sources of light.

Insects like glowworms and fireflies emit light in darkness. There are certain kinds of fish that emit light. The light given out by living bodies is called bioluminescence.

》》 Luminous Bodies

Objects that give out or emit light energy by themselves are called **luminous** bodies. Heavenly bodies like the sun, the stars are self luminous bodies.

Objects like a burning candle, an electric bulb, a red hot filament are **man-made luminous** bodies.

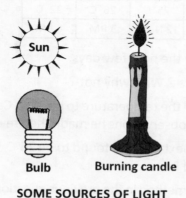

Sun

Bulb   Burning candle

SOME SOURCES OF LIGHT

> **INSIGHT**
>
> *Poke a hole in a piece of paper, hold it in sunlight so that the solar image is the same size as a coin on ground, and then determine how many coins would fit between the ground and the pinhole. That's the same number of solar diameters that would fit in the distance from the Earth to the Sun.*

»»» Non-Luminous Bodies

The bodies that do not emit light energy of their own, but reflect the light energy falling on them and hence visible to us are called ***non-luminous*** bodies.

Eg. The Moon, objects around us, books, chairs, buildings, trees, etc.

The Moon appears bright by ***reflecting*** the sunlight falling on it.

Medium

The ability of light to pass through various substances is not the same.

a) *Transparent:* It is a medium (substance) through which light can be propagated easily.

Eg. Glass, water, etc.,

b) *Translucent:* It is a medium (substance) through which light is propagated partially.

Eg. Oil, ground glass, etc.,

c) *Opaque:* It is a medium (substance) through which light cannot be propagated.

Eg. Wood, iron, etc.,

»»» Ray of Light

The path along which light travels is called a Ray of light.

A ray of light

NOTE: A single ray cannot be isolated from a source of light.

»»» Beam of Light

A collection of light rays along a definite direction is called a ***Beam of light***.

»»» Parallel beam of light

A collection of large number of rays that travel parallel to each other is called a ***Parallel beam of light***.

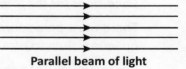

Parallel beam of light

»»» Convergent beam of light

A collection of light rays coming from different directions that meet at a point is called a ***Convergent beam of light***.

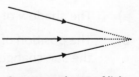

Convergent beam of light

»»» Divergent beam of light

A collection of light rays that start from a point and travel in various directions is called a ***Divergent beam of light.***

NOTE: A very narrow beam of light is called Pencil of light.

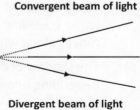

Divergent beam of light

The property of light travelling in a straight line is called **Rectilinear propagation** of light.

Everyday phenomena of rectilinear propagation of light

a) Formation of **days and nights** proves that light travels in straight lines. If this were not so, then light would have curved around the Earth and there would have been sunlight during night too.

b) When a beam of sunlight enters a dark room through a ventilator, we can see the light rays travelling in a straight lines.

c) The beam of light coming from the projection room in a **cinema hall** proves that light travels in straight lines.

d) The light coming from small **laser torches** and used as pointers is because light travels in straight lines.

e) Formation of **shadows** occurs as light travels in straight lines.

》》》 Shadows

Shadow of an object is formed due to blocking of light. Shadow is an area of darkness formed on the screen when an opaque body is placed in between a screen and a source of light. A shadow consists of two regions, umbra and penumbra.

》》》 Umbra

A region of total darkness is called Umbra. No ray of light enters this region.

》》》 Penumbra

A region of partial darkness that surrounds the umbra is called Penumbra. If the source of light is smaller than the object then both umbra and penumbra are formed.

Conditions for the formation of shadows

There must be a source of light, an opaque body to obstruct the path of light and an opaque screen to receive the shadow as it cannot be formed in air.

Characteristics of a shadow

a) The shadow of an object is formed on the opposite side of the light source.

b) The position of the shadow changes with the position of light source. As the position of the sun changes, the length and direction of a shadow also changes.

c) The position of the shadow changes with the movement of an object. For example while travelling in a moving train during day time, you will notice that the shadow moves along with the train.

d) The shadow of an object may be bigger, smaller or of the same size as that of the object, depending upon the size of the source of light.

►►► Formation of a shadow when extended source of light is smaller than an apaque body.

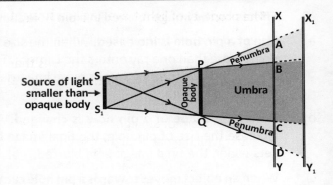

SS$_1$ is the source of light (glowing electric bulb or candle flame), PQ, an opaque body and XY the screen, such that the source of light is smaller than the opaque body. From the figure it is clear that the region BC does not receive any ray of light, either from point S or from point S$_1$, and hence, is an **umbra**. However, the region AB, receives light from point S and the region CD from point S$_1$, and hence, gets partially lighted up. Thus AB and CD are **penumbral regions.**

►►► Formation of a shadow when extended source of light is bigger than an apaque body.

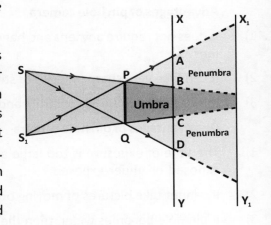

SS$_1$ is the extended source of light (such as fluorescent tube), PQ an opaque body smaller than extended source and XY the screen. From the figure it is clear that the region BC does not receive any ray of light, either from point S or from point S$_1$ and hence is an **umbra**. However, the region AB, receives light from point S and the region CD from point S$_1$, and hence, get partially lighted up. Thus, AB and CD are **penumbral regions.**

►►► Pin hole camera

A **pin hole camera** uses the principle of **rectilinear propagation** of light. It produces a **real** image that is much **smaller** than the object and is also **inverted** (upside down).

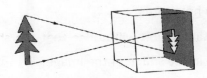

> The pinhole camera was used for the first time in the 16th century and was called camera obscura

In olden days, pin hole cameras without lens were being used to take photographs of **still objects.**

Effects on the image formed in a pin hole camera in various situations

a) **Size of a pin hole is increased:** When the size of a pin hole increases, then from a given point more than one ray enters the camera. These rays strike at different points on the screen, thereby forming two or more images. These images overlap and finally give rise to a blurred image.

b) **When the shape of a pin hole is changed:** As long as the change in shape does not increase the size of pin hole, the final image is not affected. However, in case pin hole gets wider, the final image gets blurred.

c) **When an object moves towards a pin hole camera:** The size of the image increases and so its luminosity also increases. It is because intensity of light increases as the object moves towards the pin hole. Reverse happens when the object moves away from the pin hole.

d) **When the screen moves towards a pinhole :** The size of the image decreases, but its luminosity increases. It is because the light energy entering the camera spreads over a smaller area.

Advantages of pin hole camera

1) It does not require any lens and hence, the image is completely free from the defects of lenses.

2) It can take very sharp pictures of still objects.

3) It is cheap and easy to construct and operate.

Disadvantages of pin hole camera

1) The time of exposure is too large and uncertain. Thus, the final image is either over-exposed or under-exposed.

2) It cannot take pictures of moving objects.

3) If pin hole becomes wider, then the final image is blurred.

Characteristics of image formed in a pin hole camera

1) Image is real, i.e., it can be taken on a screen.

2) Image is inverted.

3) Image is generally smaller than the size of the object; unless the distance of the object from the pin hole is less than the width of the pin hole camera.

4) Image is always in focus, i.e., it requires no focussing.

5) The shape of the pin hole produces no difference in the shape of the image.

6) It has no lens and hence, it is free from the defects of lens.

NOTE: The image of an object that can be caught on a screen is called Real image.

⯈⯈⯈ Reflection of light

Returning of light ray passing through an optical medium into the same medium from the surface of second medium is called Reflection of light. It is of two types: Regular and irregular.

> **INSIGHT**
> *Would you like to become rich ? Be the first to invent surface that will reflect 100 % of the light incident upon it.*

When a parallel beam of light falls on smooth, highly polished surface like a mirror, still surface of water, steel etc., *regular* reflection takes place. As a result *clear images* are formed.

When the surface is *irregular*, the reflected light is scattered in all directions, hence *no clear image* is formed. Such kind of reflection is known as irregular reflection.

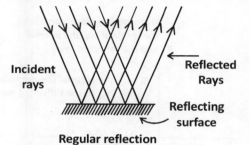
Incident rays · Reflected Rays · Reflecting surface
Regular reflection

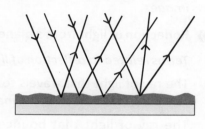
Irregular reflection

Note : The image of an object that can be caught on screen is called a **Real image**. Light rays cannot bend like sound waves.

Example : You can hear sound from a loud speaker even when you are not able to see it (i.e, behind a wall). But you cannot receive light rays from the source behind a wall.

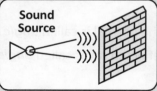
Sound Source

Light Source

⯈⯈⯈ Plane mirror

Mirrors at home give a clear image of an object because of regular reflection of light rays from its shiny glass surface. A mirror can be used to change direction of light due to reflection.

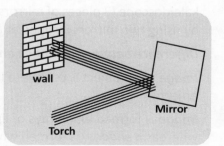
wall · Mirror · Torch

Characteristics of image formed by a plane mirror

a)   The image formed is **virtual**

b)   The image is **erect**.

c)   The size of image is **same** as that of the object.

d)   The image is formed **as far behind** the mirror, as the object is in front of it.

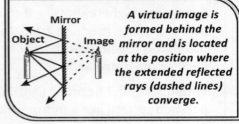

A virtual image is formed behind the mirror and is located at the position where the extended reflected rays (dashed lines) converge.

e)   The image is **laterally inverted** i.e. left hand side of the object appears as right hand side of the image and vice versa.

NOTE: The image of an object that cannot be caught on the screen is called a Virtual image.

》》》 Reflection of light from a plane surface

Terms related to reflection of light

a)   The ray of light that travels towards the reflecting surface is called **an incident ray**.

b)   The ray of light that bounces off the reflecting surface into the same medium is called **reflected ray**.

c)   The point on the reflecting surface where the incident ray hits the surface is called point of **incidence**.

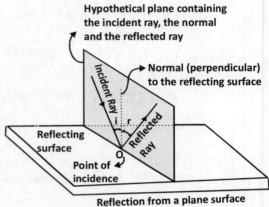

Reflection from a plane surface

d)   The perpendicular drawn at the point of incidence to the reflecting surface is called **normal**.

e)   The angle between the incident ray and the normal is called **angle of incidence**.

f)   The angle between the normal and the reflected ray is called **angle of reflection**.

Uses of plane mirrors

Plane mirrors are used as looking glasses, in solar cookers for heating, to make a kaleidoscope (3 pieces of mirrors combined in the form of a triangle) and in a periscope by using two mirrors inclined at an angle of 45°.

Difference between an image and a shadow

i)   **Image** of an object is complete in all details, whereas **shadow** is the dark outline of an object.

ii) **Image** is formed when rays of light, diverging from an object, converge at the screen, whereas **a shadow** is formed when the rays of light are obstructed by an opaque body. Speed of light in vacuum is 3×10^8 m s^{-1}.

Solved Examples

>>> **Example 1 :**

How do we see an object ?

Solution:

Light rays from the source get reflected from the object and reaches the eyes. Light creates a sensation of vision upon reaching the eyes.

We can see things when the object is a source of light **(OR)** the reflected light from the object reaches our eyes.

Note: Light from very distant objects like stars take years to reach our eyes. So, even though the stars may have changed their position, we still see them in their old places.

>>> **Example 2 :**

Classify the following materials as transparent (P), translucent (Q) and opaque (R)

Cardboard, air, glass, tracing paper, plastic scale, muddy water, brick, polythene, earth.

Solution:

>>> **Example 3 :**

A boy made holes in three cardboards of equal size. He mounts them on a table in such a manner that they are at the same height and in a straight line. He can see the lead of the pencil on the opposite side through the hole of first board.

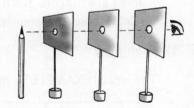

What will happen if he disturbs one of the boards from its position ?

Solution:

》》》 Example 4 :

Why can't we see the shadow of a bird or an aeroplane flying high up in the sky ?

Solution:

The bird is too small as compared to the diameter of the sun. The umbra formed by the bird is so small that it finishes in the air. The penumbra formed by it is very large and very faint. Thus, it is hardly visible. Effectively, no shadow is formed on the Earth.

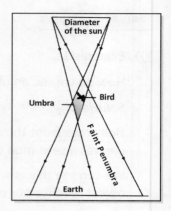

》》》 Example 5 :

A boy uses a periscope to see objects over a wall. What are objects X and Y ?

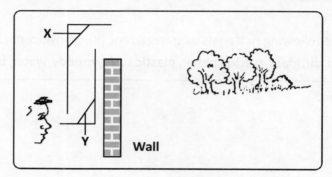

Solution:

X and Y are mirrors. Mirrors are used because they reflect light well to allow images of objects to be seen clearly, over a wall.

》》》 Example 6 :

The word "EXAMPLE" is placed facing a plane mirror. Write the correct mirror image.

Solution:

Concept Map

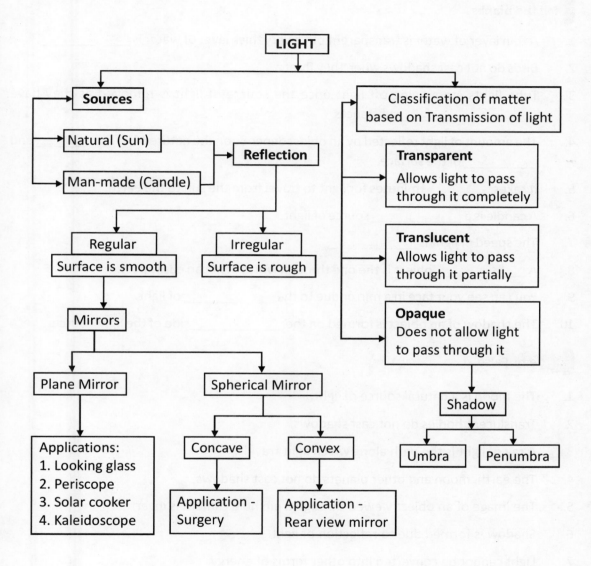

Basic Practice

Fill the blanks

1. A thin layer of water is transparent but a very thick layer of water is _____.

2. Birds do not cast shadows when they fly at a _____.

3. Tube lights stop giving off light once the source of light is removed as they have _____ substances.

4. The amount of light reflected by an object depends on the nature of _____ and _____ of the surface.

5. It takes _____ minutes for light to travel from the sun to the earth.

6. A candle is a _____ source of light.

7. The speed of light is _____.

8. A _____ object is the one through which light can easily pass.

9. You can see your face in a mirror due to the _____ of light.

10. The shadow of an object is formed on the _____ side of the light source.

True or False

1. The moon is a natural source of light.   (   )

2. Translucent bodies do not cast shadows.   (   )

3. A ray of light is the path along which light travels.   (   )

4. The earth, moon and other planets do not cast shadows.   (   )

5. The image of an object viewed through a pin hole camera is inverted.   (   )

6. Shadow is formed due to reflection of light.   (   )

7. Light cannot be converted into other forms of energy.   (   )

8. Light cannot be absorbed by any object.   (   )

9. The television screen is a light source.   (   )

10. Shadows are always of the same shape and size as the object.   (   )

Further Practice

》》》 *Write the **correct option** as your answer on the line provided.*

1. **Which of the following emits light ?**   _____
  (A) Cricket (B) Glow worm (C) Bat   (D) Rat

2. **Light shows a propagation that is**   _____
  (A) rectilinear. (B) random. (C) curvilinear. (D) none of the above.

3. **Translucent objects**   _____
  (A) allow light to pass through them.
  (B) radiates light.
  (C) allow a partial amount of light to pass through them.
  (D) does not allow light to pass through them.

4. **Which of the following reflects light the best?**   _____
  (A) A mirror   (B) A piece of paper
  (C) A cloth   (D) A wooden table

5. **Metals are shiny because of**   _____
  (A) reflection of light.   (B) rectilinear propagation of light.
  (C) absorption of light.   (D) radiation of light.

6. **Increase in the size of the hole in a pin hole camera will result in a** _____
  (A) sharp image.   (B) blurred image.
  (C) erect image.   (D) multiple image.

7. **Umbra and penumbra are clearly visible when** _____
  (A) the source of light is small and the object (opaque) is big.
  (B) the source of light is big and the object (opaque) is small.
  (C) both source of light and the object are big and placed far apart.
  (D) both source of light and the object are small and placed nearer to each other.

8. **Penumbra is seen**   _____
  (A) inside the umbra.   (B) outside the umbra.
  (C) away from the umbra. (D) none of the above

9. **In which material can light transmit the best ?** _____
  (A) A glass block   (B) A piece of blank paper
  (C) A spot of black ink (D) A placid lake surface

10. You cannot see a burning candle by using a bent pipe as light   _____

(A) gets bent along the pipe.   (B) travels in straight line.

(C) gets reflected.   (D) gets absorbed.

11. You can see round the corners by using a   _____

(A) magnifying glass.   (B) pin hole camera.

(C) telescope.   (D) periscope.

12. The shadow below a tree has bright spots in it because   _____

(A) leaves attract the light.

(B) the light bends around the leaves to form circular spots.

(C) the gaps between the leaves act as pin holes.

(D) leaves reflect light.

13. Penumbra is formed only by a/an   _____

(A) point source of light.   (B) extended source of light.

(C) both (A) and (B)   (D) none of the above

14. At which of the following times, the length of a shadow of a tree will be the longest   _____

(A) At 9 AM.   (B) At 11 AM.   (C) At 12 PM.   (D) At 1 PM.

15. A window glass is usually   _____

(A) transparent. (B) translucent. (C) opaque.   (D) none of the above.

16. Which of the following allows light to pass through easily ?   _____

(A) A metal plate   (B) A glass of water

(C) A book   (D) A cloth

17. We see the moon because it   _____

(A) emits light.   (B) absorbs sunlight.

(C) reflects sunlight.   (D) is a luminous source.

18. Which of the following absorbs light the best ?   _____

(A) A mirror   (B) A piece of white paper

(C) A black wallet   (D) A green leaf

19. Some times, when we pass under a tree covered with large number of leaves, we notice small patches of sunlight under it. These circular images are images of   _____

(A) a tree.   (B) leaves.   (C) the sun.   (D) none of the above.

20. A torch shines onto a star-shaped card. A shadow is formed on the screen behind the card. When the torch is moved away from the card, what will happen to the shadow ? _____

(A) It decreases

(B) It increases

(C) It decreases before it increases   (D) It changes its shape

21. Identify the correct image of English alphabet P when seen through a plane mirror as shown below. _____

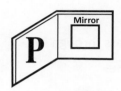

(A)   (B)   (C)   (D)

22. A boy cannot see his image on a paper but his image is formed in a pinhole camera as shown below. What are the characteristics of his image ? _____

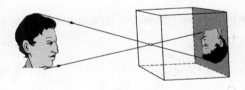

(A) Virtual, erect, small

(B) Real, inverted, small

(C) Virtual, inverted, magnified

(D) Real, erect, magnified

>>> *Write the **correct options** as your answer on the line provided.*

1 Glass is widely used in _____

(A) spectacles.   (B) windows.   (C) fish tanks.   (D) cupboards.

2. Which of the following is a natural luminous source of light ? _____

(A) Candle   (B) Glow worm   (C) Torch light   (D) Sun

3. Opaque objects _____

(A) allow light to pass through them.

(B) do not allow light to pass through them.

(C) emit light.

(D) can reflect the light falling on them.

4. **Which of the following is / are translucent substances ?** _____

 (A) Ground glass   (B) Muddy water

 (C) Iron plate   (D) Leather belt

5. **The image formed through a pin hole camera of an object is** _____

 (A) virtual and erect.   (B) inverted and small.

 (C) magnified and erect.   (D) real.

6. **An opaque object forms a shadow when placed in light because** _____

 (A) light gets refracted.

 (B) It does not allow light to pass through it.

 (C) light travels in a straight line.

 (D) light produces umbra and penumbra.

7. **A shadow moves on the screen** _____

 (A) when the source moves parallel to the screen.

 (B) when the object moves parallel to the screen.

 (C) change in colour of source of light.

 (D) all of the above.

8. **Which of the following is/are not light sources ?** _____

 (A) A planet   (B) A star

 (C) A metal strip   (D) A burning candle

9. **Which of the following is/are the properties of a plane mirror image ?** _____

 (A) The image is the same size as the object.

 (B) The image is virtual.

 (C) The image is laterally inverted.

 (D) The image is real.

10. **Which of the following is/are NOT true?** _____

 (A) A pin hole camera can take pictures of moving objects.

 (B) A ray of light that bounces off the surface of a mirror is called a reflection.

 (C) The image formed on the screen of a pin hole camera is not inverted.

 (D) A region of total darkness is called umbra.

Conceptual Questions

1.   What is the difference between the sunlight and the moonlight? Is the moon a natural source of light ?

     (Hint: Moon reflects the light from sun and appears bright to us. It does not have its own light)

2.   Distinguish between umbra and penumbra.

3.   How can the shadow of an object be made bigger than the object itself ?

4.   How does the shadow of a tree change its position and size throughout the day ?

5.   Does the shadow of a moving vehicle or train move at the same speed?

6.   What are the bright spots created by sun rays entering a room through a small hole in the door or a window ?

7.   Why is it difficult to see a clean glass door?

8.   We can see our image in a mirror but not in a piece of wood eventhough both are opaque. Why?

9.   Given below are objects P, Q and R with a light ray incident on each of them.

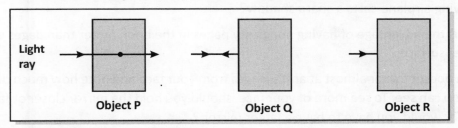

     (a) Which object reflects the light?

     (b) Which object P, Q or R, absorbs the light ?

     (c) Which object P, Q or R, transmits the light ?

     (d) Give one example of   (i) Object P   (ii) Object Q   (iii) Object R

10. Why are silvered surfaces used behind light bulbs in torches ?

11. If you hold a transparent object in the sun, do you see anything on the ground which will give a hint that you are holding something in your hand?

Brain Nurtures

1.   When light rays fall on a dry cloth it appears bright. But when the same light is incident on the wet cloth it appears dark. What could be the reason ?

2.   Place a transparent coloured paper in front of the beam of the torch light with an object in front of it. What is the colour of shadow ?

3.   How do opaque and transparent bodies differ with regard to reflection ?

4.   How can an inverted image of an object be obtained with a plane mirror ?

5.   In the given figure, the bulb is moved in the direction shown by the arrow. How does the shadow of the sphere change ?

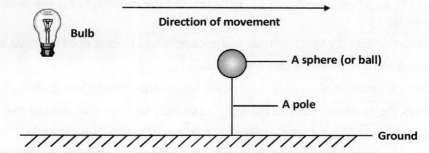

6.   How does a sundial work ? What is the disadvantage of the sundial ?

Application Based

1.   Why does a high-flying airplane cast little or no shadow on the ground below, while a low-flying airplane casts a sharp shadow?

2.   What is the advantage of having nonglossy pages in the book rather than pages with a glossier surface ?

3.   Hold a pocket mirror almost at arm's length from your face and note how much of your face you can see. To see more of your face, should you hold the mirror closer or farther away, or would you have to have a larger mirror ?

4)   A rear-view or a side-view mirror is a very important part of a vehicle as far as safety is concerned. One may even be fined for removing such mirrors from their vehicles. Try to answer the following questions about rear-view mirrors.

    a)   Would it be desirable for a rear-view mirror to provide a large field of view or a very narrow field of view ?

    b)   Given here is the ascending order of field of view provided by 3 types of mirrors placed at the same distance from our eyes.

        Concave mirror < plane mirror < convex mirror.

        Which type of mirror should be used as a rear-view mirror ?

    c)   You must have observed that it is written, "Objects in mirror are closer than they appear" on side-view mirrors of bikes.

        Will the same be written if a plane mirror is used as a side-view mirror ? If not, what would be written ?

Crossword

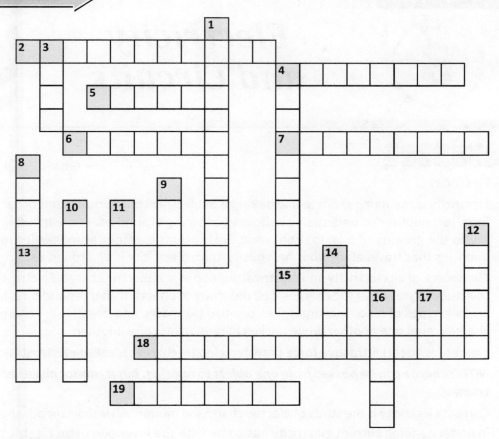

ACROSS

2   A medium through which light is propagated.
4   Motion of moon around the earth.
5   A vertical measurement of length.
6   The inversion that takes place in image formed by a plane mirror.
7   The motion of a violin string.
13 The surface on which reflected light is scattered in all directions.
15 The amount of surface occupied by an object.
18 The light given out by living bodies.
19 A region of partial darkness in a shadow.

DOWN

1   Principle of pinhole camera.
3   A body is not moving with respect to surroundings.
4   Motion of a body in a curved path.
8   100th part of a metre.
9   The property of light that makes opaque objects visible.
10 The heart beat of a resting normal person.
11 It causes in us the sensation of vision.
12 A body does not allow light energy to pass through it.
14 The SI unit of length.
16 A unit common in all systems of units.
17 A natural source of light.

Chapter 3

Electricity and Circuits

Synopsis

>>> Electricity

Electricity is the name given to a wide range of electrical phenomena that occur in one form (or) another or underlie just about every thing around us. From lightning in the sky to the glowing of a lamp, from what holds atoms together as molecules to nerve impulses that travel along your nervous system, electricity is all around us.

The source of all electricity and electrical phenomena is electric charge. Electrostatics is the study of static electric charges. i.e., the study of effects of charges under rest. There are two types of electric charges, i.e., positive (+) charge and negative (–) charge. Like charges repel one another while unlike charges attract one another.

The repulsive (or) attractive force between electric charges is called electrostatic force.

NOTE: Charge can be passed from one object to another, but it cannot be either lost or created.

Current electricity is the study of electric charges in motion. An important advancement in understanding current electricity has come with the invention of an electric cell.

>>> Electric Cell

An electric cell is a source of electricity. It produces electricity from the chemicals stored inside it. It consists of a metal cap marked as the positive terminal while a metal disc is marked as the negative terminal. On connecting it across a device it utilizes the energy developed by it. When the chemicals in the electric cell are used up, the electric cell stops producing electricity. A group of cells make up a battery. Thus in a cell, chemical energy is converted into electrical energy.

>>> Electric Circuit

A continuous conducting path, between the terminals of source of electricity (such as a cell or a battery) is called electric circuit. When an arrangement in which electric current flows in a complete path is called a circuit. When an electric bulb is connected through two wires, one connected to positive terminal while the other wire to negative terminal of an electric cell, then such an arrangement is termed as a simple electric circuit.

Open electric circuit: An electric circuit in which flow of current stops, because of open switch is called open electric circuit.

Closed electric circuit: An electric circuit in which current flows continuously, because the switch is closed is called closed electric circuit.

A simple electric circuit consists of a source of electricity (electric cell) , connectors (wire) and utilizers of electricity, eg: bulb.

To represent an electric circuit, certain components and symbols used are given in the table below.

Components	Cell	Battery	Tap key/switch	Resistor	Fuse	Bulb
Symbols	⊣⊢	⊣⊢⊣⊢	⟋	⟋W̌W̌⟋	⟋⟋	⊗

⟫⟫⟫ Electric Current

Electric current is the amount of electric charge that flows through a cross-section of wire in a unit time. It is measured in amperes (A). In an electric circuit, the current is due to the flow of free electrons, and difference in potential. This is similar to the flow of water from a higher region to lower region. In a circuit, the direction of conventional current is from positive terminal to negative terminal and electron flow is from negative terminal to positive terminal.

For continuous flow of electrons, the circuit must be complete with no gaps. Most of the circuits have more than one device (bulb, heater, fridge etc.,) that receive electric energy. These devices are commonly connected in a circuit in one or two ways: series or parallel.

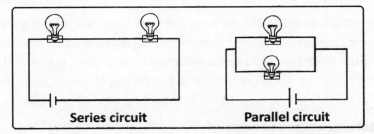

Series circuit	**Parallel circuit**

When connected in series, they form a single pathway for electron flow between two terminals.

In series connection, the total emf is equal to the sum of their individual emf's. If three cells, 1.5 V, 2.5 V and 3 V cells are connected in series, then resultant emf is equal to 7 V.

When connected in parallel, they form branches, each of which is a separate path for the flow of electrons.

In parallel connection, the total emf is equal to the highest emf of the given emf's. If three cells 1.5 V, 2.5 V and 3 V cells are connected in parallel, then resultant emf is equal to 3 V.

⟫⟫⟫ Electric Switch

An electric switch is a device that is used between two points or terminals either to break the electric circuit or to complete the electric circuit and enable the current to flow. An open switch does not allow any flow of current.

⟫⟫⟫ Fuse

A fuse or a circuit breaker is provided as a safety measure for our domestic electricity connection and in many machines.

To prevent overloading in circuits, fuses are connected in series along the supply line. In this way, the entire live current must pass through the fuse. A fuse rated for 20 A will pass only 20 A current and not more than that. A current above 20 A will melt the fuse, which 'blows out' and breaks the circuit.

⟫⟫⟫ Electric Conductors and Insulators

Materials that allow electricity to pass through them are called **good conductors** of electricity, e.g., metals like copper, aluminum etc., Materials that do not allow electricity to pass through them are called **bad conductors** or insulators, e.g., wood, plastic, ceramic etc., Human body is a good conductor of electricity. All precautions must be taken to avoid contact with electric current, while handling electrical appliances.

Important characteristics of electricity

a)   It can be changed (converted) to other forms of energy easily.

b)   It can easily be transported (with the help of wires) to various appliances and other places, though overhead cables.

c)   It can be generated (produced by converting other forms of energy) in desired quantities and with relative ease.

Solved Examples

》》 Example 1 :

Look at the electric circuits using materials P and Q as shown. Why the bulb does not glow in circuit 2 ?

(A) P is a conductor and Q is an insulator

(B) P is an insulator and Q is a conductor

(C) P and Q are insulators

(D) One of the P and Q is a conductor and the other is an insulator.

Solution: (D)

The bulb glows in 1st case implies current can flow through P or Q or both. The bulb does not glow in the 2nd case implies one of P and Q must be an insulator, but we cannot say which one.

》》 Example 2 :

Draw a circuit using bulb, battery and connecting wire. List out the material that can be used for the connecting wire to conduct electricity and enable the bulb to glow.

> *Solution:*

》》 Example 3 :

Given below are some objects that will make the bulb glow if used in a circuit. Circle the materials that makes the bulb glow.

Copper coin, ceramic cup, wooden piece, silver chain, paper clip, eraser.

》》 Example 4 :

Write the correct energy changes that take place to enable a bulb to glow in the given figure ?

> *Solution:*

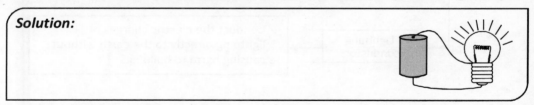

Concept Map

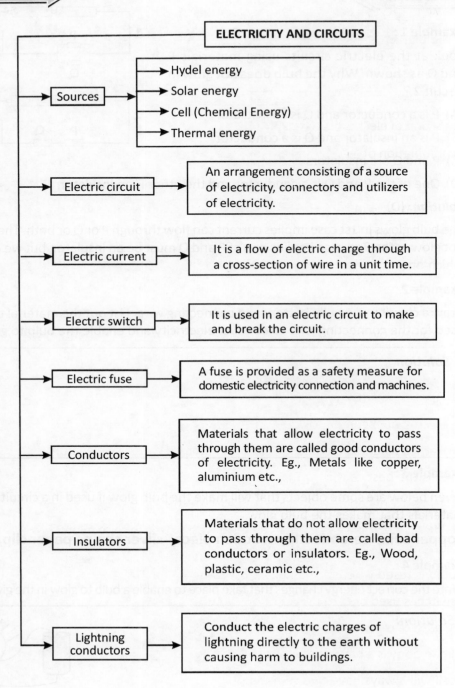

ELECTRICITY AND CIRCUITS

Sources
- → Hydel energy
- → Solar energy
- → Cell (Chemical Energy)
- → Thermal energy

Electric circuit → An arrangement consisting of a source of electricity, connectors and utilizers of electricity.

Electric current → It is a flow of electric charge through a cross-section of wire in a unit time.

Electric switch → It is used in an electric circuit to make and break the circuit.

Electric fuse → A fuse is provided as a safety measure for domestic electricity connection and machines.

Conductors → Materials that allow electricity to pass through them are called good conductors of electricity. Eg., Metals like copper, aluminium etc.,

Insulators → Materials that do not allow electricity to pass through them are called bad conductors or insulators. Eg., Wood, plastic, ceramic etc.,

Lightning conductors → Conduct the electric charges of lightning directly to the earth without causing harm to buildings.

> **Basic Practice**

Fill in the blanks

1.   Electricity is a form of _____.

2.   Electric current is the flow of _____.

3.   The SI unit of electric current is _____.

4.   A combination of a group of cells joined in series is called a _____.

5.   In a _____ circuit, there is more than one path for the current to flow.

6.   A device used to make or break contact in an electric circuit is called _____.

7.   A tester is used by an electrician to find the flow of _____.

8.   In an electric circuit, the direction of current is taken to be from _____ to _____ terminal of the cell.

9.   A circuit breaker provided in our domestic electric supply is essentially a _____.

10.   A microwave oven used in our home converts _____ energy into _____ energy.

True or False

1.   An electric bulb contains a very thin filament of tungsten.   (   )

2.   Two lamps when connected in series are dimmer than a single lamp   (   )

3.   Silver is the best conductor of electricity.   (   )

4.   Electric current can flow through walls of a house.   (   )

5.   The metal electric wires can be replaced with plastic wire to allow flow of current.   (   )

6.   A bulb is fused when its filament is broken.   (   )

7.   A switch is used only to prevent flow of current.   (   )

8.   The path of electric current is called a circuit.   (   )

9.   Human body is a bad conductor of electricity.   (   )

10.   A cell will always have two terminals.   (   )

Further Practice

>>> *Write the **correct option** as your answer on the line provided.*

1. Ritu has set up a circuit as shown. What must she put in the position X to make the bulb glow more brightly ?

    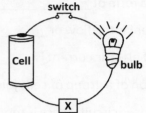

    (A) Bulb

    (B) Wire

    (C) Key

    (D) Cell

2. Electric current is

    (A) rate of flow of charge.   (B) interaction of charges.

    (C) flow of voltage.   (D) flow of electric potential.

3. In which of the following circuits will the bulb or bulbs glow the brightest?

    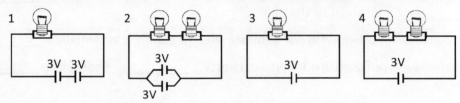

    (A) 1   (B) 3   (C) 4   (D) 2

4. A fuse rated 5 A will allow _____ current to pass through it.

    (A) 5 A.   (B) Less than 5 A.

    (C) More than 5 A.   (D) both (A) and (B).

5. The wire of a fuse should have

    (A) low melting point.   (B) more thickness.

    (B) very high resistance.   (D) higher strength and low conductivity.

6. Copper is used for making electric wire instead of iron as it

    (A) is a better conductor than iron.   (B) is cheaper than iron.

    (C) can make higher power than iron.   (D) is lighter than iron.

7. Which part in an electric circuit changes electrical energy into another form of energy ?

    (A) Energy source   (B) Wire

    (C) Switch   (D) Load (bulb etc.)

8.   Commonly used safety fuse wire is made up of   _____

(A) tin.   (B) lead.

(C) nickel.   (D) an alloy of tin and lead.

9.   What will happen if the interior of an electric bulb is filled with oxygen gas ?   _____

(A) The bulb will glow brighter.   (B) The bulb will last long.

(C) The bulb will not last long.   (D) The bulb will not glow at all.

10.   Overhead electric cables passing through poles are NOT insulated because   _____

(A) insulation will cause energy loss.

(B) air is a bad conductor.

(C) the wires will get heated.

(D) it is costly.

11.   The metal disc provided at one end of a common cell is the   _____

(A) switch.   (B) positive terminal.

(C) negative terminal .   (D) spring.

12.   If the two terminals of a cell are connected directly with a wire, then   _____

(A) more electrical energy will be stored in the cell.

(B) no current will flow in the wire.

(C) the chemicals get used up very fast.

(D) nothing will happen.

13.   Wires used in our home are usually covered with insulators like
      plastic or rubber. This is done to   _____

(A) prevent rusting.   (B) make handling easier.

(C) make the wire durable.   (D) prevent shock and short circuit.

14.   In a battery, electrical energy is obtained from   _____

(A) storage of electricity.

(B) chemical reactions.

(C) interaction between positive and negative terminals.

(D) none of the above.

15.   A bulb glows when   _____

(A) current flows through its filament.   (B) it is heated.

(C) battery is replaced.   (D) shown to light.

16. The device which makes contact between two terminals is called a _____

(A) filament.   (B) circuit.

(C) cell.   (D) switch.

17. A piece of glass _____

(A) is a conductor.   (B) is an insulator.

(C) is a semi conductor.   (D) none of the above.

18. The main function of a switch is to

(A) save the energy.   (B) make or break a circuit.

(C) make the bulb glow easily.   (D) prevent electric shocks.

19. Which of the following is the correct method of setting a circuit ?   _____

20. Nidhi has two bulbs connected across two cells in a simple circuit. How can she make the bulbs glow dimmer ?   _____

(A) Replace one cell with a piece of chalk.

(B) Replace one cell with a piece of wire.

(C) Replace one bulb with a piece of wire.

(D) Replace one bulb with another cell.

21. Which forms of energy obtained from electricity is/are used in our homes ?   _____

(A) Light   (B) Sound

(C) Heat   (D) All of the above

22. Electric current flows through a water heater, CD player, bulb and a fan. The correct energy conversion is from electrical energy to _____ energy.   _____

(A) Light, wind, sound, heat

(B) Heat, sound, light, mechanical

(C) Wind, sound, heat, light

(D) Sound, light, wind, heat

23. A boy used a piece of thread to connect the terminals of a battery in a circuit with a bulb. What will happen to the bulb ? _____

(A) It does not glow   (B) It fuses

(C) It glows   (D) It bursts

》》》 *Write the **correct options** as your answer on the line provided.*

1. The filament of an electric bulb _____

(A) has high resistance.   (B) has high melting point.

(C) is very thin.   (D) undergo oxidation easily.

2. Which of the following statements is/are correct ? _____

(A) The path along which electric current flows is called a circuit.

(B) A switch allows current to flow in a circuit when closed.

(C) Bulb in a simple circuit glows when the switch is open.

(D) In an electric circuit, current flow is due to ions.

3. One of the reasons why a bulb does not glow even if correct connections are made is because _____

(A) the battery is dead.   (B) filament is broken.

(C) switch is not closed.   (D) the electric wires are made up of copper.

4. Which of the following statements is/are not correct ? _____

(A) A thick fuse wire can withstand high current

(B) A mobile phone uses a storage cell

(C) Electric current can jump a gap, if it is too small (of the order of mm)

(D) A battery sometimes has one terminal only

5. Electric heaters used for cooking have the filament or the heating coil on a plate made up of clay because it is a _____

(A) bad conductor of heat.   (B) bad conductor of electricity.

(C) good conductor of heat.   (D) good conductor of electricity.

6.   Which of the following statements is/are not correct ? _____

(A) When electric circuit is closed, no current flows through it.

(B) Rubber is a good example of an electric insulator.

(C) Mica is an example of good conductor of electricity.

(D) Switch is a device used to close or open an electric circuit.

7.   What are the possible risks when an electrical appliance is used in wet places ? _____

(A) The fuse blows   (B) The user gets an electric shock

(C) Fire occurs   (D) More water overflows out the appliance

8.   What is the advantage of connecting bulbs in parallel? _____

(A) Each bulb can be controlled by a switch.

(B) If one bulb blows, the other bulbs are not affected.

(C) Adding more bulbs in parallel do not make the other bulbs dimmer.

(D) Bulbs fuse faster.

Conceptual Questions

1.   How does the electric current flow in a circuit connected to a cell ?

2.   Rajesh connected a bulb to a battery. But, the bulb did not glow. What could be the reason ?

3.   What happens to the brightness of a bulb, when it is powered by two cells instead of one connected in series ?

4.   What are the ways by which insulators are used along with conductors to help prevent electric shocks to human body ?

5.   How does the electric current flow between the two terminals of a battery ?

6.   Why is a switch used in a circuit ?

7.   Why do human beings get electric shock ?

8.   We do not get shock under overhead electric wires. Why ? (Hint: Air is an insulator)

9.   Why does a fuse blow off when high voltage enters into mains ?

10.   What happens when an electric circuit is open ?

Brain Nurtures

1. Why is the filament in an electric bulb made from tungsten?

2. What is the main aim of arranging cells in series ?

3. What will happen to a fuse wire in a circuit if there is excess current flowing through it ?

4. Six dry cells, each with a voltage of 1.5 V, are placed in series. However, two of the cells have been connected wrongly as shown in the diagram.

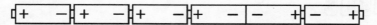

   What is the overall voltage of this arrangement of dry cells?

5. What is the advantage of connecting bulbs in parallel in a circuit?

Application Based

1) Consider the circuit shown below that has 5 switches and 3 bulbs.

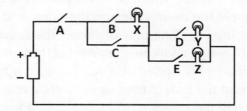

   Answer the following based on the given circuit diagram.

   a) If only switches A and B are closed, which bulb(s) would glow ?

   b) Which are the switches that must be closed to make bulb X glow ?

   c) Can bulb X glow without any other bulb glowing ?

   d) Can bulb Y glow without any other bulb glowing ?

   e) Which switches must be closed to make only bulbs Y and Z glow ?

2) A neutral object (i.e., an object that is neither positively charged nor negatively charged) has no positive or negative charges in it. True or False ?

3) Which of the following is a device used to store electrical energy ?

   (A) Switch   (B) Conducting wires

   (C) Battery   (D) Capacitor

Magnets

4

>>> **Magnetism**

Magnetism is one of the fundamental properties of matter. The ore of iron called **magnetite** (Fe_3O_4) is the first magnet known. Magnets attract materials made up of iron, cobalt or nickel. These are called **magnetic materials**. Other materials which do not get attracted by a magnet are called **non–magnetic materials** e.g. paper, plastic, wood, etc. The metals like silver, sodium etc., are not magnetic materials and cannot be magnetised or used to make magnets. All magnets have two poles - north pole and south pole. The end of the suspended magnet, which points towards the north, is called the north - seeking pole (or) simply the **north pole** and the other end which points towards the south is called the south - seeking pole or simply the **south pole** of the magnet. The magnetic strength of a magnet is more prominent at the two ends known as the **poles of a magnet**. When a magnet is dipped into iron filings, it is noticed that the iron filings cling in large numbers at the **ends** of the magnet and there are hardly any filings clinging to the middle portion of the magnet.

>>> **Properties of Magnet**

(a) **Like poles repel and unlike poles attract**. If the N pole of a bar magnet is brought near the 'N' pole of a suspended magnet, there is a repulsion. On the other hand if the N pole of a magnet is brought near the 'S' pole of a suspended magnet both will attract each other as shown in the figure.

(b) Repulsion and **not** attraction is the sure test for a magnet. This is because magnets can also attract magnetic materials like iron, which are not magnets themselves. Hence we, cannot say whether the other material is a magnet or just a magnetic material. However, if the other material gets repelled when a particular end of a magnet is brought near it, we can certainly say that the other material is a magnet.

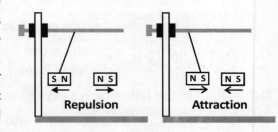

(c)   The Earth is imagined to be a huge magnetized sphere of iron containing a huge permanent magnet in its core. The south seeking magnetic pole of the Earth is located in the northern hemisphere near the geographic north and the north seeking magnetic pole is located at a diametrically opposite point in the southern hemisphere, near the geographic south. This is referred to as ***terrestrial magnetism***.

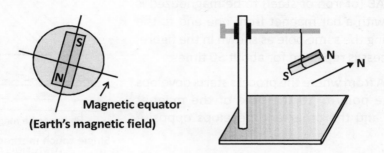

Magnetic equator
(Earth's magnetic field)

All magnets align in the north-south direction of the earth when suspended freely. A bar magnet when suspended always aligns itself to north – south as shown in the figure. This property is known as directive property. Using directive property of magnet magnetic compasses are devised.

(d)   When a magnet is broken, each piece acts as an individual magnet.

(e)   A magnet on heating, tapering or rough handling loses its magnetism.

Uses of magnets

Magnets are commonly used in refrigerator doors and cabinets for secured locking. Magnets are also used in music systems to enhance sound quality. In offices pin holders use magnets. In a junk yard a frame with a huge electromagnet is used to separate iron scrap from other wastes for recycling. Magnets are also used in TV, computers, ATM cards, CDs, Audio cassettes etc.

⫸ Methods of magnetisation

An artificial magnet is prepared by moving a natural magnet in contact over an iron bar in a particular direction or with the help of electricity.

(OR)

There are two methods of magnetising a piece of iron or steel to make it an artificial magnet. (i) By stroking or mechanical method and (ii) By electrical method.

By Mechanical Method

A bar of iron or steel can be magnetised by using either one or two permanent magnets as described below:

(i) *Single Touch Method*

The bar AB (of iron or steel) to be magnetized is stroked with a bar magnet from one end to the other using the same pole as shown in the figure. This process is repeated for about 50 times.

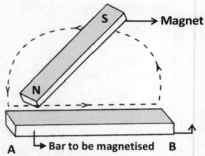

The end A from where the process starts develops the same polarity to the pole of the magnet stroking and the other end develops opposite polarity.

Single touch method of magnetizing

(ii) *Double touch or Divided touch method*

The bar AB to be magnetized is stroked with two bar magnets of equal strength by placing their opposite poles in the middle of the bar and stroking one in the clockwise direction and the other in the anti-clockwise direction as shown in the figure. On reaching the ends, the magnets will be lifted and brought back to the middle position. This process is repeated several times. The ends of the bar AB acquire opposite polarity to the poles of the magnets stroking on them. This method is more efficient than the single touch method since it can make stronger magnets.

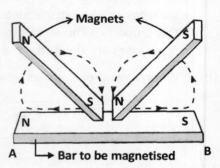

Double touch method of magnetizing

Electrical Method of Magnetisation

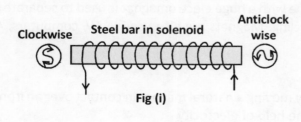

Fig (i)

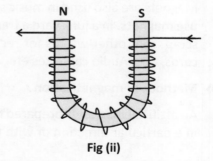

Fig (ii)

Powerful magnets are commercially produced by electrical methods. The electrical method is based on the principle that a *long coil carrying current* behaves like a *magnet*. A long coil carrying current is called a solenoid. If a bar of iron or steel is kept inside the solenoid and current is passed through the coil, the bar inside it gets magnetized.

By winding insulated copper wires in opposite directions on the two arms of a 'U'–shaped iron or steel piece and on passing current in the winding, a **horse shoe magnet** can be obtained. Magnetisation by electric current method creates more powerful magnets than other magnetization methods as stroking.

NOTE:

(i)   If the bar placed inside the solenoid is that of steel, it becomes a permanent magnet. However, if soft iron is used in place of steel, it behaves as a strong magnet as long as current flows in the solenoid. Thus it behaves as a temporary magnet.

(ii)   We can easily determine the polarity of this magnet. In figure (i) it can be seen that looking from the left end of the solenoid, the current is flowing in the clockwise direction and so that end of the bar becomes the south pole of the magnet. Looking from the right end of the solenoid, it is found that current is flowing in the anti-clockwise direction and hence this end of the bar becomes the north pole of the magnet.

⟫⟫⟫ Electromagnets

The magnets which lose their magnetism as soon as the cause producing them is removed, are called **temporary magnets**. Eg. Electromagnets and the magnets made from soft iron are temporary magnets. The magnets which do not lose their magnetism, when the cause producing them is removed are called **permanent magnets**.Eg. The magnets made from steel are permanent magnets.

⟫⟫⟫ Uses

(i)   They are used in a number of electrical devices, such as electric bell, telephone, telegraph, radio, transistor, television, loud-speaker.

(ii)   They are used in fans, motors, mixers, room coolers, etc.

(iii)   They are used for lifting heavy iron loads.

(iv)   Magnets are used in making magnetic stickers and magnetic toys.

(v)   Audio cassettes, mobile phones, ATM/credit cards, CDs and computers use magnetism to store data. Hence, magnets should be put away from these objects.

(vi)   A magnetic compass is used by the sailors for navigation in the sea.

⟫⟫⟫ Demagnetisation

Permanent magnets can be demagnetised by the following methods.

(a)   Heating

(b)   Hammering

(c)   Using alternating electric current.

Magnetic Keepers

Magnetic property decreases if magnets are not stored properly. To keep them safe, two magnets should be kept in pairs with their unlike poles on the same side. They must be separated by a non–magnetic material like wood with two pieces of soft iron (keepers) placed across their ends. A horse–shoe magnet should be stored with a piece of iron across the poles as shown below.

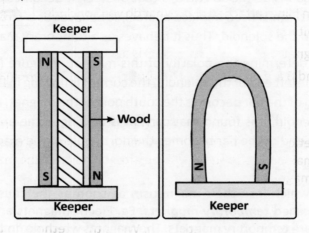

Solved Examples

Example 1 :

Five steel needles were fixed to the hooks of a small brass disc are suspended freely as shown below. If a pole of a strong magnet is brought at the base needles from below; the needles will first be drawn apart and then will again assume a vertical position, when the magnet is brought right up to them. As the magnet is removed, the needles will again be drawn apart forming a cone shaped bunch. What happens to the steel needles ?

(A)   They turn anticlockwise   (B)   They induce south poles

(C)   They turn clockwise   (D)   They induce north pole

Solution:

>>> **Example 2 :**

Two rods A and B one of them a magnet and other a non-magnet, but of magnetic material were attracted by a strong magnetic pole as shown. The magnet was then taken near iron filings where these filings got attached to both A and B. On removal of the strong magnet it was found that only 'B' has iron filings attached to it. What do you conclude from this activity ?

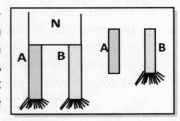

(A)   A is a magnet

(B)   B is a magnet

(C)   Both A and B are magnets

(D)   Both A and B are non–magnets

Solution: (B)

Since, the nails from rod A fall off, when the strong magnet is removed, we can say that A is the magnetic substance, which has lost its induced magnetism. On the other hand iron filings remained attached to 'B' even after removal of the magnet. This shows 'B' is a permanent magnet.

>>> **Example 3 :**

Figures show methods of magnetisation. Write the methods in the blanks.

I)   _____

II) _____

III) _____

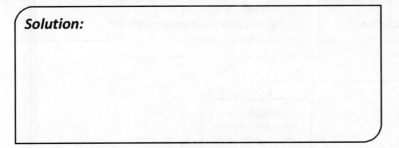

Iron piece   Iron piece   Iron piece

>>> **Example 4 :**

A student placed a magnet over 5 pins made of different materials in a trough. Which set of pins are attracted to the magnet ?

(A)   Steel, nickel, iron,

(B)   Copper, brass, nickel

(C)   Tungsten, cobalt, silver

(D)   Aluminium, bronze, chromium

Solution:

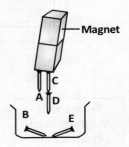

Concept Map

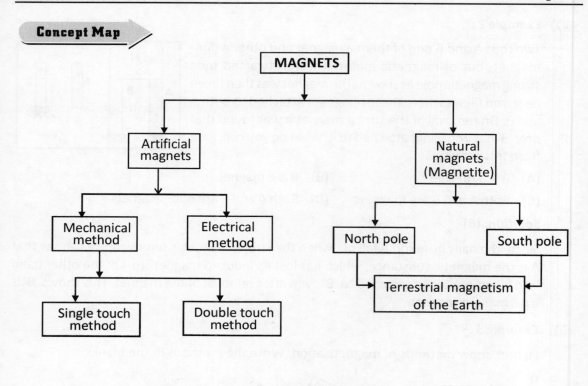

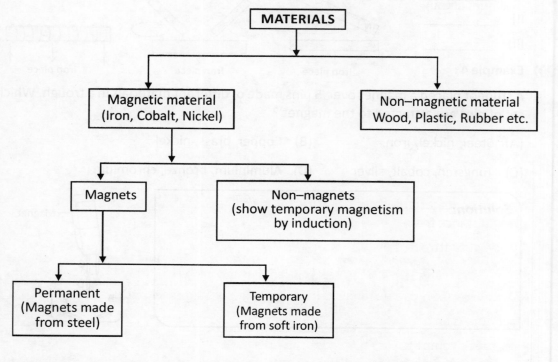

Basic Practice

Fill the blanks

1. _____ are difficult to magnetize but retain their magnetic properties for a long time.

2. Magnets made with magnetic metals have _____ magnetic properties.

3. The major advantages of artificial magnets are that they can be made in any _____ or strength as desired.

4. The distance (NS) between the north pole and south pole of a bar magnet is called the _____.

5. _____ is the temporary magnetization of a magnetic substance under the influence of a magnetizing force.

6. A magnet always has _____ poles.

7. A bar magnet when suspended freely will always align in_____ direction.

8. _____ poles of two magnets repel each other.

9. Maximum amount of iron filings will get stuck to both the _____ of a bar magnet.

10. A _____ is used by sailors to find direction in sea.

True or False

1. Earth is imagined to be a huge magnet.   (   )

2. Silver is a magnetic material.   (   )

3. A bar magnet has only one pole, either north or south pole.   (   )

4. A long coil carrying current behaves like a magnet.   (   )

5. A magnetic material will not get attracted if you keep the magnet at a long distance from it.   (   )

6. A blade gets attracted by both the poles of a magnet.   (   )

7. The north pole of a magnet will attract north pole of another magnet.   (   )

8. Artificial magnets can be made from non- magnetic materials also.   (   )

9. Magnetite is an ore of magnet.   (   )

10. A magnetic compass uses a magnetic needle to show directions.   (   )

Further Practice

》》》 Write the **correct option** as your answer on the line provided.

1. Which parts of the horse-shoe magnet shown
    in the figure has the strongest pull on some pins ?

    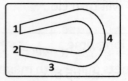

    (A) 1 and 2 only   (B) 3 and 4 only

    (C) 1, 2 and 3 only   (D) 1, 2 and 4 only

2. Harish was asked to identify a piece of soft iron put in a basket of 10
    magnets of same shape and size. Which is the easiest way of identifying
    the iron piece at the earliest ?

    (A) By picking up one magnet at a time and suspending it.

    (B) By picking up two magnets at a time and conduct repulsion test.

    (C) By bringing another strong magnet near the basket.

    (D) By dropping all magnets into water.

3. The diagram below shows a compass placed between two equally
    strong bar magnets. Identify the poles of both the bar magnets.

    (A) SS, NN   (B) SN, SN

    (C) NN, SS   (D) NS, NS

4. A compass is used for

    (A) alignment along N – S direction.   (B) to find direction on the sea.

    (C) to attract magnetic materials.   (D) both (A) and (B).

5. When two substances repel each other then

    (A) one of them must be a magnet.

    (B) both of them must be magnets.

    (C) one of them must be non-magnetic.

    (D) both of them must be non–magnetic.

6. An iron nail is suspended. A strong bar magnet is
    placed behind an iron sheet as shown in the figure,
    near the suspended nail. What will happen ?

    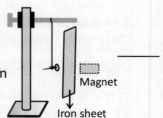

    (A) The nail will move towards the magnet due to attraction

    (B) The nail will NOT move towards the magnet

    (C) The magnet will move towards the nail

    (D) The nail will be attracted only if the 'S' pole of the magnet is kept near it

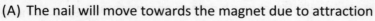

7. A small magnet Y is placed near a heavy magnet X as shown in the figure. How will the magnets move ? _____

    (A) Y will move away.

    (B) Y will turn clockwise.

    (C) Y will turn anti clockwise.

    (D) X and Y both will turn clockwise.

    Magnet X
    | N   S |

    N
    | | Magnet Y
    S

8. A ring made up of copper can be placed in which group of the above question. _____

    (A) Q   (B) P   (C) R   (D) either Q or P

9. After repeated rubbing with a magnet in the same direction, a piece of substance fails to get magnetised, it should be in the group (s): _____

    (A) P and Q   (B) Q and R   (C) Q   (D) R

10. Articles from which group(s) can be attracted by a magnet? _____

    (A) P and Q   (B) Q and R   (C) Only Q   (D) Only R

11. Articles from which group can be attracted by 'P' but cannot be attracted by other objects ? _____

P	Q	R
Magnet	Magnetic substance	Non-magnetic substance

    (A) R   (B) Q   (C) P   (D) P and Q

12. An object is repelled by a magnet. It must be placed in the group _____

    (A) P.   (B) Q.   (C) R.   (D) none of these.

13. In many household articles we can find a magnet instead of a lock or a bolt in the doors. Magnets are used in such places mainly to _____

    (A) facilitate frequent usage.   (B) ensure safety.

    (C) make the article airtight.   (D) make the article look beautiful.

14. The most suitable material to be used as the core of an electromagnet is _____

    (A) steel.   (B) iron.   (C) copper.   (D) ceramic.

15. Two ring magnets, X and Y are put through a rod as shown below. (Magnet X 'floats' above magnet Y because) _____

    (A) magnet X is lighter than magnet Y.

    (B) magnet Y is more powerful than magnet X.

    (C) the like poles of both magnets are facing each other.

    (D) the unlike poles of both magnets are facing each other.

    Rod

    Magnet X

    Magnet Y

16. Which of the following show the correct way of storing magnets ?

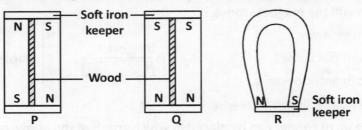

(A) P and Q only

(B) P and R only

(C) Q and R only

(D) P, Q and R

17. Which of the following produces the strongest electromagnet ?

(A) Brass core

(B) Copper core

(C) Wooden core

(D) Iron core

18. Why does a compass needle always points to the north ?

(A) The compass needle is made of a magnetic material.

(B) The compass needle is a magnet with the pointer as the south seeking pole.

(C) The compass needle is a magnet with the pointer as the north seeking pole.

(D) The compass needle is an electromagnet that is charged by rubbing when the needle is turning.

19. Kavya hung four magnets, W, X, Y and Z from string of two different lengths and placed a tray of pins below the magnets as shown below. She noticed that different number of pins were attracted to the magnets. Which order is correct about the magnets from the strongest to the weakest ?

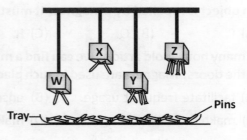

(A) W, X, Y, Z   (B) W, Y, X, Z   (C) Z, X, Y, W   (D) Z, X, W, Y

20. A very strong magnet 'A' is brought near a weak magnet 'B' with same poles facing each other, What will happen to the magnet ?

(A) Both the magnets will repel each other

(B) The stronger magnet will move away

(C) The weaker magnet will move away

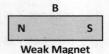

(D) Initially there will be repulsion, then the strong magnet will attract the weak magnet.

21. In the diagram shown below three bars are placed in line. X and Y are both magnets, Z is soft iron. What are the magnetic forces on X and Z due to magnet Y ?

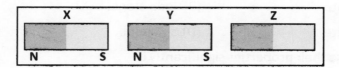

(A) Attraction, Attraction   (B) Repulsion, Repulsion

(C) Attraction, Repulsion   (D) Repulsion, Attraction

22. In the diagram shown below, three paper clips are attracted to the two poles of a bar magnet. What are the poles formed at the ends X and Y ?

(A) N–pole and S–pole

(B) N–pole and N–pole

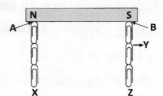

(C) S–pole and S–pole

(D) S–pole and N–pole

23. A bar magnet is cut into two pieces as shown below. Which figure correctly shows the new poles formed at the cut ends of two pieces of magnets?

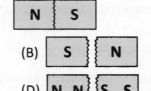

(A)    (B) [S][N]

(C) [N S][N S]   (D) [N N][S S]

24. Rakesh has one bar magnet and two iron pieces all of same size and shape. To find out the magnet he needs

(A) nothing else.   (B) a non–magnetic substance.

(C) a compass.   (D) a piece of thread.

25. Which figure shows the correct method to make artificial magnets ?

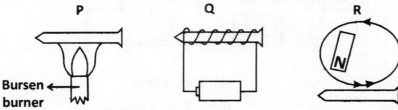

(A) P and R   (B) P and Q   (C) Q and R   (D) P, Q and R

>>>> *Write the* **correct options** *as your answer on the line provided.*

1.   **A natural magnet is known as**   _____

      (A) magnetite.   (B) lode stone.

      (C) haematite.   (D) solenoid.

2.   **Magnets lose their properties significantly if**   _____

      (A) left in the open.   (B) heated strongly.

      (C) dropped from a height.   (D) none of the above

3.   **Which of the following statements is /are not true ?**   _____

      (A) The north pole of a magnet will attract north pole of another magnet
          if they are kept very near to each other.

      (B) Artificial magnets can be made from non–magnetic materials also.

      (C) Magnetite is an ore of iron.

      (D) Isolated magnetic poles do not exist

4.   **Which of the following contains a permanent magnet in it ?**   _____

      (A) Torch   (B) Radio   (C) Fan   (D) Compass

5.   **Which of the following materials is/are not suitable for the core of an
      electromagnet ?**   _____

      (A) Steel   (B) Soft iron   (C) Copper   (D) Aluminium

6.   **Which of the following is/are magnetic material(s) ?**   _____

      (A) Steel   (B) Copper   (C) Nickel   (D) Aluminum

7.   **Observe the arrangement of magnets shown below.**

      Which of the arrangements shown is/are not possible ?   _____

      (A) 2 and 3   (B) 1 and 3 only

      (C) 1 only   (D) 1, 3 and 4 only

8.   When the S-pole of a magnet is placed near an unknown pole of another magnet, the two magnets   _____

(A) may repel each other if the unknown pole is a N-pole

(B) may repel each other if the unknown pole is a S-pole

(C) attract each other because the unknown pole is a N-pole

(D) can either attract or repel

9.   A damaged car is picked up by a crane and shifted to a safe place. Which of the following statements is true of this activity ?   _____

(A) The car is made of magnetic material.

(B) The crane uses a strong electromagnet to pick up cars.

(C) The electromagnet works only when there is an electric current flowing

(D) The crane has a permanent magnet.

10.   A permanent magnet is not used in   _____

(A) magnetic door latches.   (B) electric bells.

(C) compasses.   (D) mixers.

Conceptual Questions

1.   Where are the poles of a magnet located ?

2.   A bar magnet has no markings to indicate its north or south pole. How will you determine their poles ?

3.   How can you find out a magnet of the same size and shape kept with a number of iron bars ?

4.   Two bar magnets when brought together get stuck. What conclusions will you draw from this observation ?

5.   If a compass is kept near an iron body will it be able to show correct direction. If not, why ?

6.   What will happen if audio cassettes or CD's are kept near magnet ?

7.   What are the differences between soft and hard magnetic materials ?

8.   Does an isolated magnetic pole exist like an isolated electric charge ?

Brain Nurtures

1. What is wrong in the figure shown below ?

2. Vishnu set up the experiment as shown below. He coiled some wires around a U-shaped iron rod and connected the wires to three batteries.

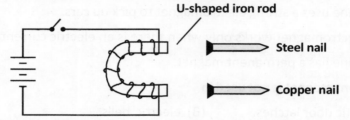

U-shaped iron rod

Steel nail

Copper nail

What happens when a steel nail and a copper nail respectively are placed at the two ends of an iron rod after the switch is closed ?

3. A class teacher showed an activity in the class where he made the iron pins to suspend one below the other by using a magnet as shown below. How was it possible ?

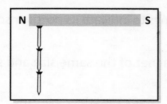

4. A small thin iron nail is suspended from a light fire proof thread. A strong magnet is placed near the nail and a flame from a gas burner is produced between the nail and the strong magnet.

The flame licks the nail, when it is attracted by the magnet and then gets out of the flame to come back to its original position. After a lapse of time, the nail will again be drawn to the flame. What causes the to and fro movement of the nail ?

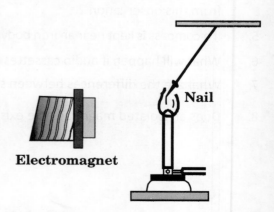

Electromagnet

Nail

5. When a piece of bar magnet is brought near bar X, part A was attracted to the South pole of the bar magnet. What type of material is bar X and also indicate the poles developed by part A and part B of bar X ?

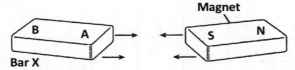

6. Is the magnetic field of the Earth stronger near the middle of the Earth (in Mexico) or at the bottom of the Earth (in Antarctica) ? Explain your answer.

Application Based

1) Golu was intrigued by one of his own observations. He read that the earth has a huge magnet in its core. He also observed that when he dropped a nail, it fell to the ground. From this, Golu concluded that it is the magnetism of earth that pulls objects towards the ground.

    Is Golu's conclusion correct ? If not, can you give a counter example ?

2) Why is it that a magnetic needle always has to align itself in the North-South direction when suspended freely ? Why can't the earth's magnet realign itself along the direction of a magnetic needle ?

3) When a magnetic needle is suspended by a thread tied exactly at its centre, will it align itself vertically (perpendicular to the floor) or horizontally (parallel to the floor) ? Assume the experiment is conducted in India.

4) In the previous question, if the experiment is conducted in Antarctica, how would the magnet align itself ?

5) In the movie Dhoom 2, the thief Mr. A makes a can of Coca Cola come into his grip from a distance all by itself, just by opening his palm. How is it possible ?

6) The figures given below show a coil wound on a soft iron core P, and an identical coil wound on a steel core Q. Five nails were attracted to each of them when the current is on. What are the probable number of nails still attracted to P and Q after the switches were opened ?

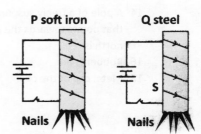

    (A) 0, 0   (B) 0, 5

    (C) 5, 0   (D) 5, 5

Crossword

ACROSS

3 A steel bar can be converted into a magnet by passing current through it.
5 Things that keep magnet safe.
6 Device used for finding geographic directions.
7 A naturally occurring magnet.
9 The path of electric current.
12 Glows in an electric bulb.
14 A pole of a freely suspended magnet that points towards the geographic north is
16 Rubber is an
18 Metal cap of the cell.

DOWN

1 Demagnetise a permanent magnet.
2 Magnetic attraction is maximum at
4 Magnetism on the earth.
6 Things that allow the current to flow through them.
8 It makes (or) breaks the circuit.
9 Sources to produce electricity in a cell.
10 A substance capable of attracting pieces of iron.
11 Like poles.
13 A high voltage is obtained by connecting cells.
15 There is no flow of electric current in the circuit, when the switch is
17 A component in the atmosphere that is a bad conductor of electricity.

Chapter 5

Forces

Synopsis

Force

A force is a **push** or a **pull** that one object exerts on another. We cannot see force but we can feel its effect(s).

Energy is needed to exert a force.

A force can cause the following :

(a) Move a stationary object

Ex: A stationary supermarket trolley will move if we exert a pushing force on it.

(b) Stop a moving object

Ex: A rolling marble will stop if we exert a push force on it.

(c) Change the shape of an object.

Ex: A piece of plasticine can be remoulded by pulling or pressing against it.

(d) Change the direction of a moving object.

Ex: A flying shuttlecock will change its direction when we strike it with a racket.

(e) Change the speed of a moving object.

Ex: A moving toy car will move faster if we continue to push it in the same direction.

The amount of force applied on an object affects

(a) the distance moved by the object.

(b) the speed at which the object moves.

Different kinds of Forces

Contact forces :

All forces that act on a body directly or through a connector are called contact forces.

Eg : Frictional force, muscular force.

Frictional Force

Friction is a force that opposes sliding. It acts at the surfaces of contact in the direction **opposite to the relative motion**. Friction is produced when two surfaces rub against each other. There is more friction between rough surfaces and less friction between smooth surfaces.

Muscular Force

The force caused by the action of muscles in our body is known as muscular force.

》》》 Friction is useful in many ways. Some advantages of friction are:

(a)   It enables us to walk without slipping.

(b)   It enables us to grip objects.

(c)   It produces heat. Our palms get hot when rubbed against each other.

(d)   It stops the wheels of a moving vehicle when we step on the brakes.

(e)   It holds nails and screws in the wooden furniture.

(f)   Enables us to write on a paper with pencil or pen.

Friction can also cause problems. It has the following disadvantages:

(a)   It causes **wear and tear** of our shoes, slippers and car tyres.

(b)   It slows down a moving object and does not allow us to move fast.

We can reduce friction with lubricants such as oil, grease or wax. We can also use ball-bearings, rollers and wheels. In some instances, we can also sprinkle powder or flour.

》》》 Non-contact forces :

The force that does not need a direct contact with a body, but acts or through space is called non-contact or force at a distance.

Eg :   Gravitational force, magnetic force and electrostatic force.

Gravitational Force

The Earth exerts a pulling force on all objects that have mass. This force of attraction between the Earth and other objects is known as gravity. Gravity also exists on other planets, the Sun, the moon, etc., However, because these objects have different sizes, their gravitational forces exist is varying amounts.

(a)   The Sun's gravitational force is so immense that it keeps the planets in the Solar system revolving around it all the time. The Sun's gravity also ensures that the planets revolve in fixed orbits.

(b)   The moon's gravity however is lesser. The gravitational pull on the moon is approximately only **one - sixth** of the Earth's. On the Moon, we weigh approximately one-sixth our weight on Earth because the moon has weaker gravitational force than the Earth.

(c)   The pull of gravity on an object gives the object its weight. An object with **more mass** has **more weight**.

(d)   We are weightless in space, in places where gravity is not felt.

Magnetic force

A magnet exerts a pulling force on objects made of magnetic materials such as iron, steel, cobalt and nickel. **Like** poles of magnets exert a **push** force against each other. They repel each other. We call this as magnetic force of repulsion. Unlike poles of magnets exert a pull force towards each other. They attract each other and this is known as magnetic force of attraction.

Electrostatic Force

The force erected by a charged body on another charged or uncharged body is known as electrostatic force. All objects have two types of electric charges, positive charges and negative charges. Ordinarily, these charges are equal in number. So, they balance out each other and objects appear to be electrically neutral. However, due to various reasons when an object has more negative charges than positive changes, it becomes negatively charged. Similarly an object with more positive charges than negative charges becomes positively charged.

Objects that have opposite charges attract each other, while objects that have similar charges repel each other. The electrical charges that build upon an object are static until they are released under the influence of other charged bodies. The force applied by these static charges is called electrostatic force.

》》》 Measurement of force

Force is a physical quantity which can be measured. The SI unit of force is newton (N). The most common device used to measure force is a spring balance.

Spring balance

A spring balance works on the principle that a spring gets stretched or compressed when a force is applied on it. Larger the force, more is the stretch or compression. So, the force is measured by measuring the stretch or compression in the spring.

Representation of force

A force may be small or large. The size or stretch of a force is called its magnitude. The direction in which a force act is also important. Thus, to represent a force, both its magnitude and direction are to be taken into account. A force is represented by a straight line with an arrowhead at the end. for example, a force of 10N can be expressed as $\xrightarrow{\text{10 N}}$.

The length of the straight line represents the magnitude and the head of the arrow shows the direction in which the force is acting. Generally the magnitude of the force is written along the length of the straight line.

Resultant of force

We have already learnt the effects of a single force on a body. But there are a large number of situations where more than one force acts on an objects simultaneously. In such cases, all the forces acting on an object can be replaced by a single force that has the same effect on the body. This single force is called the resultant force.

When forces act in the same direction

If two or more forces act along the same direction, the resultant force is equal to the sum of the magnitudes of all the forces being applied individually. The resultant force will act along the same direction as the individual forces.

When forces act in opposite direction

If two or more unequal forces act on the same object along opposite directions, the resultant force is the difference of their magnitudes. The resultant force will act along the direction in which the force is greater. But if the forces acting in opposite direction are of equal magnitude, they balance out each other, and the object does not move in any direction.

Units of Force

Unit of force is called **newton** (symbol N).

The unit commonly used for measuring force is called **kilogram force** (symbol kgf). **One kgf** is the force required to lift a body of mass 1 kg vertically upward. For smaller forces the unit is gram force (symbol gf). **One gram force** (1 gf) is the force required to lift a mass of 1 g vertically upward.1 kgf is equal to 1000 gf.

>>>> **Solved Examples**

>>>> **Example 1 :**

An experiment was conducted to find the amount of force needed to move a 100 g load each over four different surfaces using a spring balance. Which surface will show the smallest reading on the srping balance?

(A) Wood   (B) Concrete   (C) Metal   (D) Glass

> **Solution:**
>
>
>
>

>>>> **Example 2 :**

Mrs. Rama was driving her car at a high speed. She saw a boy walking in front of her and she quickly stepped on the brakes and her car stopped about 1 metre away from the boy.

(a)   How did the brakes help Mrs. Rama's car to stop ?

(b)   Would it have been more or less likely for the car to knock down the boy if the incident happened on a rainy day ? Explain the reason for your answer.

Solution :

(a)   Friction opposes sliding so it can cause a moving object to slow down and stop. The car stopped because all of its kinetic energy was converted to other forms of energy while it worked against the extra friction produced by the brakes.

(b)   Less friction is produced between surfaces that are wet or slippery. Thus, the car would move over a longer distance before all its kinetic energy was converted to other forms of energy. The car would eventually stop.

>>> **Example 3 :**

Look at the activities shown below. In which activity is the gravitational force useful?

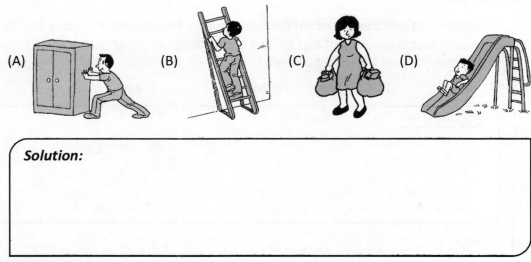

(A)   (B)   (C)   (D)

Solution:

>>> **Example 4 :**

Shiva and Hari wanted to play on the see-saw of level height as shown below in figure - **1**.

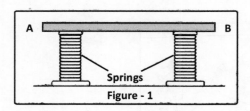

Figure - 1

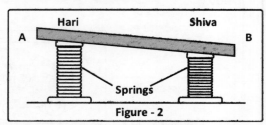

Figure - 2

(a)   When Hari got onto the see saw first at end A, the spring got compressed. Why ?

Solution :

(a)   A spring is compressed when a push is applied on it. Hari's weight was the pushing force that compressed the spring at end A.

(b)   Shiva then got onto the see-saw at end B. From the figure 2 shown above, who was heavier, Shiva or Hari ?

Solution:

Concept Map

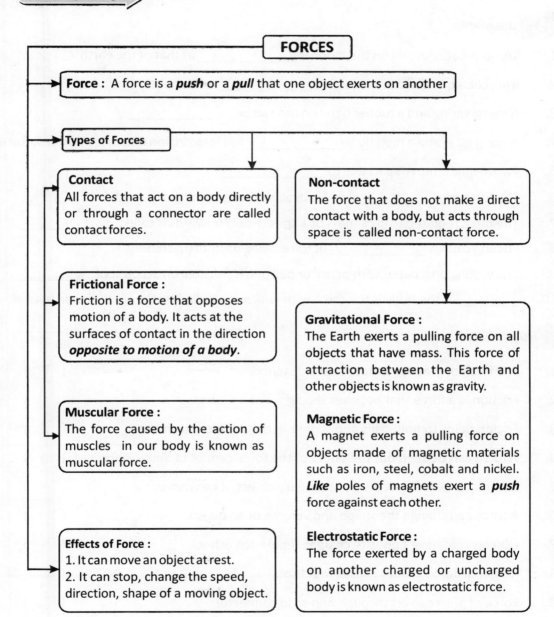

FORCES

Force : A force is a *push* or a *pull* that one object exerts on another

Types of Forces

Contact
All forces that act on a body directly or through a connector are called contact forces.

Non-contact
The force that does not make a direct contact with a body, but acts through space is called non-contact force.

Frictional Force :
Friction is a force that opposes motion of a body. It acts at the surfaces of contact in the direction *opposite to motion of a body*.

Muscular Force :
The force caused by the action of muscles in our body is known as muscular force.

Effects of Force :
1. It can move an object at rest.
2. It can stop, change the speed, direction, shape of a moving object.

Gravitational Force :
The Earth exerts a pulling force on all objects that have mass. This force of attraction between the Earth and other objects is known as gravity.

Magnetic Force :
A magnet exerts a pulling force on objects made of magnetic materials such as iron, steel, cobalt and nickel. *Like* poles of magnets exert a *push* force against each other.

Electrostatic Force :
The force exerted by a charged body on another charged or uncharged body is known as electrostatic force.

Basic Practice

Fill the blanks

1.   The gravitational pull on the moon is _____ as that of the earth.

2.   Iron, cobalt, and nickel are called _____ materials.

3.   A metal spring and a rubber band on use can be _____.

4.   Among glass and a mud floor_____ has least friction due to it smooth surface.

5.   Two magnets move apart due to _____.

6.   The force of _____ always attracts objects towards the earth.

7.   The force required to lift a mass of 1 kg vertically upwards is called _____.

8.   Friction causes _____ of the moving parts of machinery.

9.   The writing on a paper with pencil or ball pen is possible on account of _____.

10.   _____ of the body is the force with which it is pulled by the earth towards itself.

True or False

1.   The force of gravity cannot act at a distance.   (   )

2.   Friction is a force that opposes sliding.   (   )

3.   Friction helps to hold nails and screws in the wooden furniture.   (   )

4.   A force can be seen but the effect of the force cannot be felt.   (   )

5.   When a force is exerted on a stationary object, it can move.   (   )

6.   A force can change the shape and volume of an object.   (   )

7.   Objects that have opposite charges repel each other.   (   )

8.   Magnetic force always causes repulsion.   (   )

9.   Force of push can act through non-rigid connector.   (   )

10.   Frictional force is a non-contact force.   (   )

Further Practice

》》 *Write the **correct option** as your answer on the line provided.*

1.   **Which statement describes both magnetic force and gravitational force?** _____

      (A) The force is both a pulling and a pushing force.

      (B) The force exists even if there is no physical contact.

      (C) The unit of the force is joules (J).

      (D) The force is only able to act on objects made of certain materials.

2.   **A box is given a push across the floor. It comes to a stop shortly after the push. Which one of the following reasons explains why this happens?** _____

      (A) Gravity is acting on the box in the direction opposite to the box's movement.

      (B) Friction is acting on the box in the same direction of the box's movement.

      (C) Friction is acting on the box in the direction opposite to the box's movement.

      (D) The heat produced by the box's movement slows down the box.

3.   **Alvin carelessly dropped some steel pins into a jar of liquid. He tried to remove the pins by moving a magnet slowly over the surface of the jar. The pins were not attracted to the magnet. Which one of the following reasons is most likely to be?** _____

      (A) The jar is made of a non-magnetic material.

      (B) The jar is made of a magnetic material.

      (C) Alvin moved the magnet over the surface of the jar too slowly.

      (D) The pins were not magnetic.

4.   **Fitting special trains and train tracks with magnets allows the trains to float above the tracks. This reduces _____ and allows the trains to move _____.** _____

      (A) Friction between the trains and the tracks ; slower

      (B) Friction between the trains and the tracks; faster

      (C) The weight of the trains ; faster

      (D) Magnetic force between the trains and the tracks; faster

5.   **Which one of the following does not help to reduce friction?** _____

      (A) Grease   (B) Soapy water (C) Oil   (D) Sand

6. A ball that Bala kicked was travelling in path X as shown. In which path, would the ball continue to travel? _____

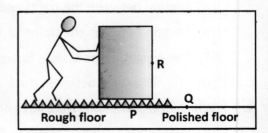

(A) 1   (B) 3

(C) 4   (D) 2

7. The frictional force is a _____

(A) contact force.   (B) force at distance.

(C) force that causes motion   (D) gravitational force.
   of a body.

8. Magnetic force always causes _____

(A) attraction.   (B) repulsion.

(C) either attraction or repulsion.   (D) electrification.

9. The SI unit of force is _____

(A) newton (N).   (B) kilogram force (kgf).

(C) gram force (gf).   (D) dyne.

10. Force of friction is _____

(A) always a disadvantage.

(B) always an advantage.

(C) sometimes an advantage and sometimes a disadvantage.

(D) neither an advantage, nor a disadvantage.

11. The deep grooves in the tyre of a tractor _____

(A) decrease friction.   (B) increase friction.

(C) make it stable.   (D) make it more attractive.

12. The force of friction _____

(A) increases with the roughness of a body.

(B) decreases with the roughness of a body.

(C) is not affected by the roughness of a body.

(D) none of these

13. Ram pushes the box by applying a force of 500 N horizontally so that the box slides along the floor as shown. Find the point where the frictional force acting on the box is maximum. _____

(A) P   (B) R

(C) Q   (D) P, Q and R

14. Ram and Rahim are pushing a body with equal forces of 100 N each as shown. Then the resultant force acting on the body is

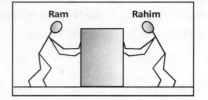

    (A) 100 N   (B) 0

    (C) 200 N   (D) 10 N

15. If no force acts on a body, it will

    (A) get deshaped.

    (B) move with increasing speed.

    (C) either remain at rest or move in a straight line.

    (D) break.

16. By applying a force of 1 N, one can hold a body whose mass is approximately equal to

    (A) 100 mg.   (B) 100 g.   (C) 1 kg.   (D) 10 kg.

17. The force of friction between two bodies is

    (A) parallel to the contact surface.

    (B) perpendicular to the contact surface.

    (C) inclined at 30° to the contact surface.

    (D) inclined at 60° to the contact surface.

18. Susan placed a toy car in front of a slope and allowed it to slide down the plane freely. The speed of the toy car increases as it goes down the slope. Which of the following force is the result of the increase in speed ?

    (A) Magnetic force

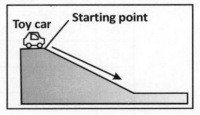

    (B) Frictional force

    (C) Gravitational force

    (D) Pushing force

19. Which force enables us to do work?

    (A) Elastic   (B) Gravitational

    (C) Muscular   (D) Frictional

20. Less friction is produced when the surfaces in contact are

    (A) slippery.   (B) wet.   (C) oiled.   (D) all the three.

21. Two persons are pushing a box in opposite directions with forces of 180 N towards right and 120 N towards left respectively. Find the resultant force acting on the box with direction.

(A) 60 N Right   (B) 120 N Left

(C) 180 N Right   (D) 300 N Left

》》》 Write the **correct options** as your answer on the line provided.

1.   **The force that makes it difficult for Anil to lift a box off the ground is**

(A) the weight of the box.

(B) the weight of Anil.

(C) due to gravity.

(D) due to friction.

2.   **Bathroom scales have springs in them to measure weight. When a weight is placed on the springs, they**

(A) are stretched.   (B) are compressed.

(C) exert a force on weight. (D) exert a force of gravity.

3.   **Which of the following is/are the effects of frictional force?**

(A) Grooves of tyres flattening after months of travelling on the road

(B) A rolling ball coming to a halt

(C) Leaves falling to the ground

(D) Grabbing hold of a pencil with your hand

4.   **In which of the following a pulling force is exerted?**

A	Leaves falling from a tree
B	An iron ball attracted to a magnet
C	Closing the refrigerator door
D	A load lifted by a pulley

5.   **David was told that force has certain effects on materials. It can change the**

(A) size of an object.

(B) direction of a moving object.

(C) chemical properties of an object.

(D) speed of a moving object.

6.   A group of children 1, 2, 3 and 4 applied the forces on the same body as shown below.

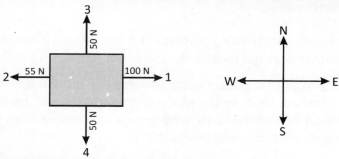

Which of the following statements is correct ? _____

(A) The net force acting on the body is 255 N

(B) The body will move towards east

(C) The net force acting on the body is zero

(D) The resultant force acting on the body is 45 N

7.   **Which one of the following statements is true ?** _____

(A) Friction helps us to twist an object.

(B) Friction is a force that opposes sliding.

(C) Objects have weight because of the frictional force between them and the Earth.

(D) More friction is produced between rough surfaces than between smooth surfaces.

8.   **Gravitational force acts on** _____

(A) all objects with mass.   (B) planets.

(C) the moon.   (D) none of the above

9.   **Which of given situation needs the greatest force ?** _____

(A) Pushing a thick needle into a thick cloth.

(B) Pulling a cart on a concrete road.

(C) Motion of a toy car on an inclined plane.

(D) Slicing a loaf of a bread with a sharp knife.

10.   **Force of gravity enables** _____

(A) the water to flow from the tap into the bucket or ground.

(B) us to fly in the air.

(C) water in the rivers to flow downward.

(D) none of the above

Conceptual Questions

1. Bending, pressing and twisting involves the use of our force. Mention a physical phenomenon that does not require the use of our force.

2. The force of gravity that pulls objects towards the ground is different on different planets. An astronaut lands on the Moon and weighs himself. He finds that he weighs less on the Moon than on the Earth. Why there is a difference in his weight if his mass is the same on both the Moon and the Earth?

3. We cannot see a force but we can usually see its effects while it interacts with objects or things around us. Give two examples of such effects.

4. State whether friction is useful in each of the situations given below .

(i)   Sharpening a pencil

(ii)   Gears (in machines) rubbing against each other

(iii) Ball bearings rubbing in roller bladders

(iv)   Striking a matchstick to light it

5. Look at the diagrams of the springs shown below.

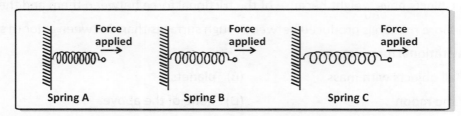

(a)   Which spring is being pulled with the largest force?

(b)   What happens when a force is applied on the springs ?

(c)   What happens to the springs when the forces applied to them are removed?

6. Beng Seng finds that the same soccer ball moves easier on a concrete floor than on a grass field. Why is this so?

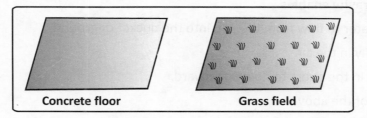

7. During basketball practice, Jayadeep jumps to shoot the ball into the hoop. After repeating this movement many times, he feels tired.

(a) Which force is Jayadeep working against when he jumps?

(b) How do we know that a force is acting on the ball after Jayadeep lets go of it ? Look at the path of the ball indicated in the diagram to explain.

8. Which type of forces help to complete the actions given below?

(a) Ability to climb up a hill

(b) Rain falling onto the ground

(c) Separating iron and steel from rubbish

9. Shirley wanted to find out whether water, oil or maple syrup would enable a marble to fall through it more easily. She filled three similar test tubes with equal amounts of water, oil and maple syrup as shown.

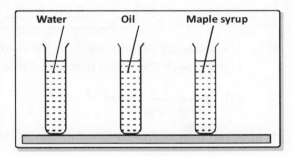

(a) List two other variables she must keep the same in order to conduct a fair experiment.

(b) Which variable was changed during the experiment ?

10. The table below shows the results of Shirley's experiment in Question 9.

Type of Liquid	Time taken for the marble to reach the bottom (seconds)			
	1st Attempt	2nd Attempt	3rd Attempt	Average
Water	1.5	1.7	1.6	1.6
Oil	2.3	2.4	2.5	2.4
Maple syrup	2.6	2.9	2.6	2.7

(a) It is easiest for the marble to fall through _____ and most difficult to fall through _____ .

(b) For each liquid, why did Shirley make three attempts to record the time taken for the marble to reach the bottom ?

Note: To conduct fair experiments, we need to repeat the same experiment several times. We find the average of the results obtained to make a conclusion. This method of conducting experiments ensures that we obtain reliable results.

Brain Nurtures

1.   The spring (2) shown below is stretched less when object B was placed under magnet A. What object is B likely to be ?

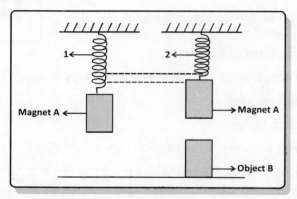

2.   The following actions are done for the distances shown below. Rearrange the actions starting with the action that uses the least force.

(1) |←——— 2 m ———→|
     Carry a 2-kg baby

(2) |←——————— 3 m ———————→|
     Carry a 5-kg - sack of rice

(3) |←——— 2 m ———→|
     Push a 2-kg trolley

(4)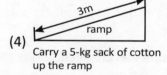
     Carry a 5-kg sack of cotton up the ramp

3.   Which one of the following diagrams does not show the use of the force indicated?

(A)
Gravitational force

(B)
Elastic spring force

(C)
Magnetic force

(D)
Frictional force

4.   We make use of forces to do a lot of things. Which of the following is the odd one out?

    (A) Kicking a ball   (B) Closing the door

    (C) Switching on the lights   (D) Stretching a rubber band

5.   Vincent conducted an experiment as shown below to determine the force required to pull a block of wood across four different surfaces.

Based on the tabulated results, arrange the surfaces from the one with the least friction to the one with the most friction.

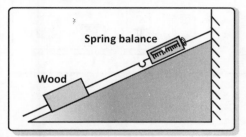

Surfaces	Force Required (N)
P	22
Q	15
R	20
S	8

6.   A ball is rolling towards the east as shown below. Which arrow correctly represents the direction of the frictional force that is acting on the moving ball?

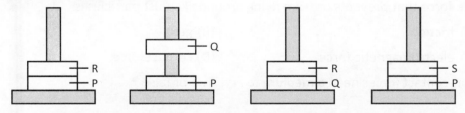

7.   Observe the figures given below.

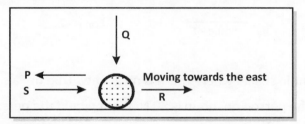

Which of the following correctly shows the properties of the above objects P,Q,R and S ?

	Magnetic	Non-magnetic	Not able to tell
(A)	P, Q	R, S	-
(B)	P, Q	-	R, S
(C)	P	Q	R, S
(D)	Q	P, R	S

8.   Four objects, P, Q, R and S were hung at the same height and when they were released, they pushed the nails into the wood as shown below.

Which of the given objects P, Q ,R and S possess the greatest gravitational force ?

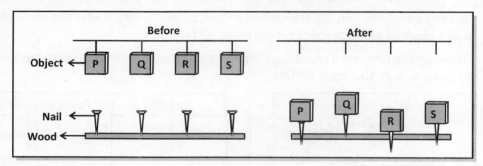

Application Based

1)   Two forces are indicated using two arrows as shown. Which force is greater in magnitude ?

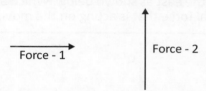

2)   Friction is absent in space, where there is no gravity. True or False ?

3)   The weight of the person on moon is 50 N. What would the person's weight be on the earth ?

4)   The force that prevents us from flying around like dust particles is

(A) friction.   (B) gravity.

(C) electromagnetic force.   (D) contact force.

5)   Non-contact forces need a medium to act. True or false ?

6 Work and Energy

Synopsis

》》》 Work

Work is said to done, if a force acting on a body is able to move it through some distance in the direction of force. Mathematically, it is measured as the product of the magnitude of force and the distance covered by the body in the direction of force. If 'F' is the applied force, 'S' is the displacement in the direction of applied force, then work done 'W' is given by, $W = F \times S$. SI unit of work is **joule** denoted by J. C.G.S unit of work is erg.

Eg : When a force of 30 N displaces a body through 8 m, in its own direction, then

Work done ($W = F \times S = 30 N \times 8 m = 240 J$)

NOTE: If nothing is actually moving, no work is done, no matter even if the greatest foce is involved.

》》》 Conditions for work to be done

There are three conditions to be fulfilled for the work to be done.

(i)   A force must be applied on the object.

(ii)   The object should move from its position of rest, there should be a displacement or there should be a change in the shape or size of the object.

(iii)   The displacement must be because of the force applied.

》》》 Situations of no work done

If any of the above-mentioned conditions is not satisfied, there is no work done. Thus, there can be no work done, if there is no force applied in situations such as reading a book, or when an object is resting on a surface, no force is applied. So, in these case no work is done.

A force is applied but there is no displacement

If a person is pushing a wall hard he is applying force, but the wall does not move. Here, eventhough a force is applied, there is no displacement. So, no work is done.

A force is applied, the object moves, but comes back to the starting point

If you push a trolley around a circular park and return to the point where you had started. In this case, a force is acting on the trolley, but there is no displacement and hence, no work is said to be done. There can be no work done, if the directions of the applied force and the displacement are at right angles (90°) to each other.

Energy

The energy of a body is defined as its capacity to do work. We cannot see energy but we can see the work done by it and its effects. Energy can move a stone, make a substance hot, produce sound and emit light.

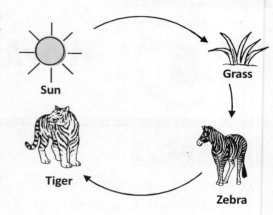

It is measured in the same units as work i.e. joule in S.I and erg in C.G.S system. Energy sources are things that provide energy. The Sun is the most important source of energy. It provides green plants with energy to make food.

All living things depend either directly or indirectly on the energy from the sun to survive. For example, the Sun provides light energy for grass to make food. The zebra which grazes on the grass gets energy from it. Finally the energy is transferred to the tiger that feeds on the zebra.

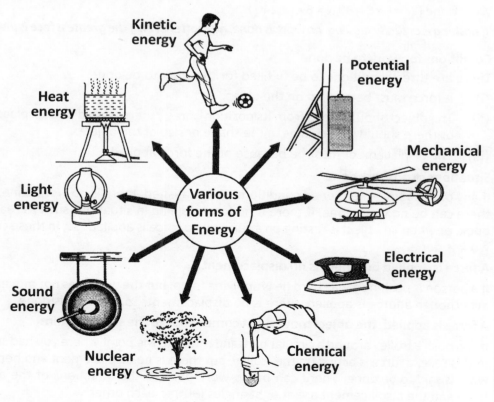

Other sources of energy include batteries, wind and running water. **Energy** can exist in various forms such as mechanical energy, heat energy, light energy, sound energy, etc., Man is able to make use of different forms of energy to do work.

Mechanical energy is of two types, namely Kinetic energy and Potential energy.

》》》 **Kinetic energy**

The energy possessed by a body by virtue of its motion is called kinetic energy. If 'm' is the mass of the body 'v' is the velocity of the body. Kinetic energy is given as

$$K. E = \frac{1}{2}mv^2$$

The kinetic energy possessed by a body of mass 5 kg and moving with a velocity of

$10 \, m \, s^{-1}$ is given as $(K.E) = \frac{1}{2}mv^2 = \frac{1}{2} \times 5 \times 10^2 = 250 \, J$.

> **Note:** 1. The more the mass of the moving body, the more is its kinetic energy.
>   2. The more the velocity of a moving body, the more is its kinetic energy.

Few examples of bodies possessing kinetic energy

1. A running train has kinetic energy.

2. A speeding car has kinetic energy.

3. The kinetic energy of air is used to run wind mills.

4. A bullet fired from a gun can pierce a target due to its kinetic energy.

5. The kinetic energy of a hammer is made use of in driving a nail into a piece of wood.

6. A stone rolling down a hill has kinetic energy.

》》》 **Potential energy**

The energy possessed by a body by virtue of its position (or) configuration is called potential energy.

Gravitational potential energy is given by, P.E = mgh

Where, m = mass of the body

g = acceleration due to gravity = $9.8 \, m \, s^{-2}$

h = height through which the body is raised.

NOTE : Potential energy is a stored energy in a body.

>>> **Some types of potential energy are:**

(a) **Elastic potential energy** is the energy that a wound-up spring or a stretched rubber band has. The tighter the spring is wound, the more elastic potential energy it possesses.

(b) **Gravitational potential energy** is the energy that a raised object has. The higher the object is raised above the ground, the more gravitational potential energy it has.

(c) **Chemical potential energy** is the energy that is stored in food, fossil fuels, batteries, etc.,

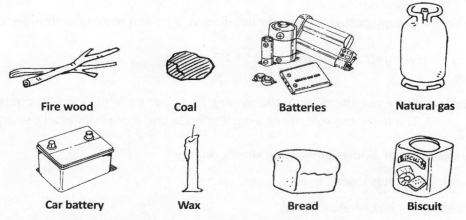

Fire wood	Coal	Batteries	Natural gas
Car battery	Wax	Bread	Biscuit

>>> **Few examples of bodies possessing potential energy**

1. The potential energy of water in dams is used to run turbines in order to produce electric energy in generators.

2. The potential energy of the wound spring of a clock is used to drive the hands of the clock.

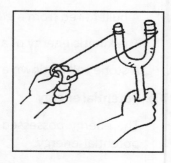

3. Due to the potential energy of the compressed spring in a loaded gun, the bullet is released with a large velocity on firing the gun.

4. Due to the potential energy of the stretched bow, the arrows go forward with a large velocity on releasing the bow.

5. When the rubber sling of a catapult is stretched, the elastic energy stored in rubber is the potential energy. It is this stored potential energy which throws the stone in the sling of the catapult in forward direction.

>**>> Uses of different types of potential energy**

(a) Potential energy in fuels can be used for cooking, moving vehicles, burning etc.,

(b) Chemical potential energy of batteries can operate our toys and machinery.

(c) Gravitational potential energy of water from dams can indirectly help to run turbines and generators to produce electricity.

(d) Elastic potential energy of wound-up springs make our toys work. For example, we wind the key of a musical box and toy car several times before the box plays music or the toy car moves.

>**>> Types of energies and their uses**

Heat Energy

Heat energy enables us to carry out our daily household chores. We use heat energy to cook our food, keep us warm, iron our clothes and dry our clothes.

(a) In power stations, heat changes the water to steam that is used to turn the turbine and drive the generators.

(b) Heat is used in manufacturing products.

(c) Sand and other chemicals are heated to very high temperatures to manufacture glass.

(d) Similarly, iron ores are heated strongly so that they melt into liquid iron before being cast into moulds.

Light Energy

The sun is our main natural source of light. Other sources of light include lamps, electric bulbs, candle, etc.,

We can use light energy in many ways.

(a) It enables us to see in the dark.

(b) The flashing light from a lighthouse warns ships of danger in the night.

(c) Traffic lights help to control traffic flow.

(d) It enables us to snap photographs with a camera. We allow light to enter the camera to focus on the object and this forms an image on the film inside the camera.

Sound Energy

Sound is also a form of energy.

(a) It enables us to communicate.

(b) It is produced by alarms and also warns us about danger.

(c) In the form of music it helps in relaxation.

(d) Sound given out by a device called SONAR and found on ships can be used to measure depths of the ocean or detect the position of under water objects.

Electrical energy

Electrical energy can be used in our homes to enable many electrical appliances to work such as rice-cookers, fans, air-conditioners, water-heaters, etc.

(a) In offices, electricity runs our computers, fax machines, printers, telephone lines and copiers.

(b) We are able to work in buildings because electric lights brighten up the place.

(c) Some means of transport such as MRT trains and cable cars run on electricity.

(d) Electricity can be used to produce electromagnets to separate metals at scrap yards.

⟫⟫⟫ Conversion of energy

Energy **cannot** be created or destroyed but it can be changed or converted into other forms of energy. This is called **Law of conservation of energy**. The total energy of an isolated system always remains constant. We have generated electrical energy in power stations. Other forms of energy can be converted into electrical energy.

(a)   A hydroelectric power plant

A tall barrier known as a dam is built across a river to impound water and raise its level. The water in the dam possesses gravitational potential energy. When the water flows downwards, the potential energy is converted into kinetic energy. The moving water rotates the turbine that is connected to a generator. The kinetic energy of the running water is then converted to electrical energy by the generator.

(b)   Energy in a bouncing ball changes in the following manner

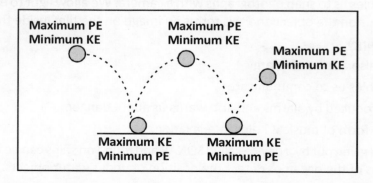

(c)   A power generation plant

When fuels such as natural gas or crude oil burn, the potential energy stored in them changes to heat energy. This heat energy heats up water, causing it to boil. The water changes from liquid state into steam. As the steam escapes, the kinetic energy of the rising steam helps to turn the turbines. The turbine inturn spins a generator that converts kinetic energy to electrical energy.

(d)   Energy conversion in a simple circuit takes place as follows:

Chemical potential energy $\rightarrow$ Electrical energy $\rightarrow$ Light + Heat energy

We encounter many changes in forms of energy in our daily activities. Different appliances convert energy in different ways. The table below shows some conversions that often take place.

Example	Energy conversion
Toy car moving down a ramp	Potential energy $\rightarrow$ Kinetic energy + Heat energy + Sound energy
Battery – operated calculator	Potential energy $\rightarrow$ Electrical energy + Light energy
Television	Electrical energy $\rightarrow$ Light energy + Sound energy + Heat energy
Electric blender	Electrical energy $\rightarrow$ Kinetic energy + Heat energy + Sound energy
Bicycle dynamo	Kinetic energy $\rightarrow$ Electrical energy
Wound-up toy car	Potential energy $\rightarrow$ Kinetic energy + Heat energy + Sound energy

Renewable sources of energy are energy sources that do not run out. These sources of energy include the Sun, running water and wind.

Non - renewable sources of energy are energy sources such as fuels that cannot be easily replaced when they are used up.

⟫⟫⟫ Fossil fuels

Fossil fuels that provide us with energy to do work can also be derived from the Sun. These are formed from the remains of organisms that lived millions of years ago. The electricity that we use as energy can be traced back to the sun as the original source. The following figure shows the energy changes leading from the sun to a coal-fired power generation plant.

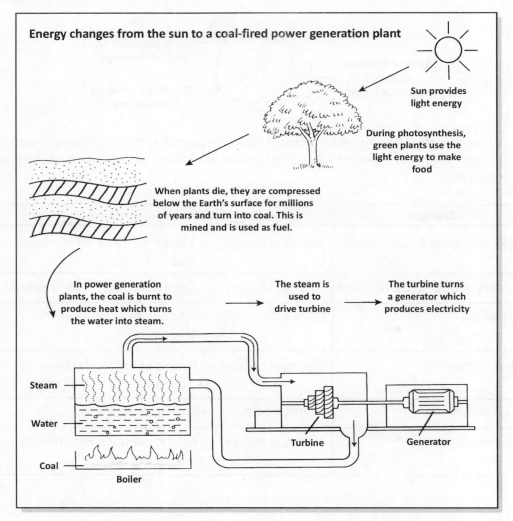

Energy changes from the sun to a coal-fired power generation plant

Sun provides light energy

During photosynthesis, green plants use the light energy to make food

When plants die, they are compressed below the Earth's surface for millions of years and turn into coal. This is mined and is used as fuel.

In power generation plants, the coal is burnt to produce heat which turns the water into steam.

The steam is used to drive turbine

The turbine turns a generator which produces electricity

Steam

Water

Coal

Boiler

Turbine

Generator

> **Solved Examples**

>>> Example 1 :

Three appliances a washing machine, a rice cooker and a radio are used in a home. Identify the energy conversion when the appliances are switched on.

	Washing machine	**Rice cooker**	**Radio**
(A)	Heat energy	Kinetic energy	Light energy
(B)	Kinetic energy	Heat energy	Sound energy
(C)	Sound energy	Heat energy	Kinetic energy
(D)	Kinetic energy	Stored energy	Sound energy

Solution:

>>> Example 2 :

A ball is being rolled down a slope as shown below.

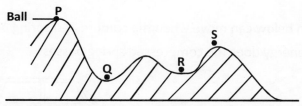

At which point does the ball has the greatest potential energy ?

(A) P   (B) S   (C) Q   (D) R

Solution:

Example 3 :

Jermaine set up an experiment as shown below. She lit the candle and placed a paper spiral above it. She noticed that the paper spiral started to spin.

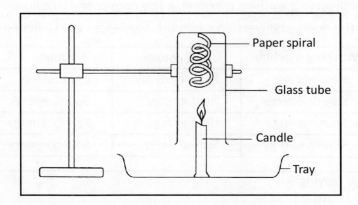

What is the purpose of leaving a gap between the tray and glass tube ?

Solution :

In order for the flame to continue burning, (so that the paper spiral continued to spin) a gap was needed between the tray and the glass tube. This is because the candle flame needs oxygen to burn. The gap allowed fresh air to enter so that the flame could receive a continuous supply of oxygen in order to continue burning.

Example 4 :

A toy car shown below can move when the compressed spring on it is released.

Which type of energy does the compressed spring possess ?

(A) Heat

(B) Sound

(C) Light

(D) Potential

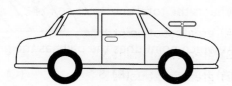

Solution:

>>>> **Example 5 :**

Four identical cars P, Q, R and S are driven at different speeds as given below.

Car P - 90 km/h, Car Q - 180 km/h, Car R - 140 km/h, Car S - 110 km/h

Arrange the cars in descending order of the amount of kinetic energy they possess.

(A) Q, S, R, P   (B) S, R, Q, P   (C) Q, R, S, P   (D) R, Q, S, P

Solution:

>>>> **Example 6 :**

A boy was playing with his drum. There were some beans placed on the table near the drum. The harder he hit the drum, the higher the beans jumped. What does the given activity prove ?

(A) Sound is a form of energy.

(B) Beans have sound energy.

(C)   The drumstick has sound energy.

(D) The boy transferred his potential energy to sound energy.

Solution : (A)

Sound produced by playing the drum made the beans jump. It proves that sound is a form of energy.

>>>> **Example 7 :**

A boy drops a ball from a height as shown below. Ignore the effects of air resistance.

What is the total energy at points 1, 2 and 3 respectively ?

(A) greatest at point 1.

(B) greatest at point 3.

(C) greatest at point 2.

(D) the same at all points.

Solution:

Concept Map

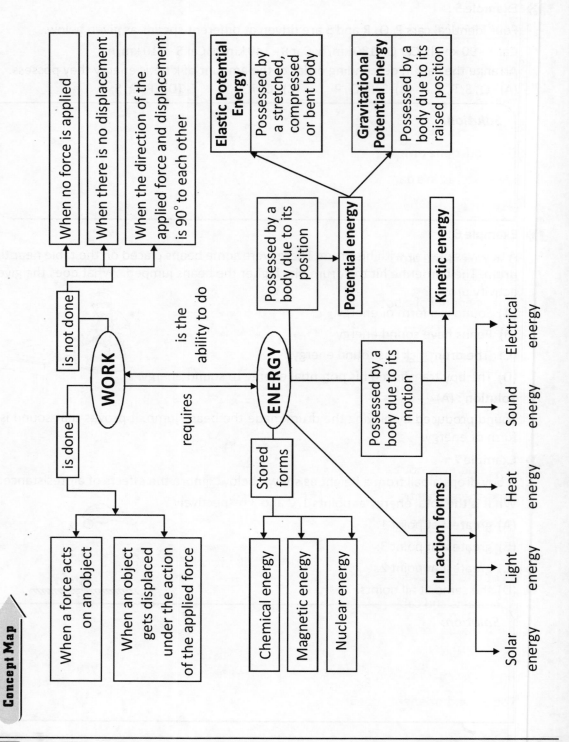

WORK

is not done
- When no force is applied
- When there is no displacement
- When the direction of the applied force and displacement is 90° to each other

is done
- When a force acts on an object
- When an object gets displaced under the action of the applied force

requires

ENERGY is the ability to do

Potential energy — Possessed by a body due to its position
- **Elastic Potential Energy** — Possessed by a stretched, compressed or bent body
- **Gravitational Potential Energy** — Possessed by a body due to its raised position

Kinetic energy — Possessed by a body due to its motion

Stored forms
- Chemical energy
- Magnetic energy
- Nuclear energy

In action forms
- Solar energy
- Light energy
- Heat energy
- Sound energy
- Electrical energy

> **Basic Practice**

Fill the blanks

1. Work is measured as a product of _____ and _____.

2. The sum of the potential and kinetic energies of a body is called _____ energy.

3. The work done on an object does not depend on its _____.

4. Water stored in a dam possesses _____.

5. A sparrow does not do work when it is at _____ on the tree

6. _____ give us the ability to do work.

7. One joule is the product of force of 1 N and displacement of _____ in the direction of force.

8. Kinetic energy of a body is the energy possessed by it on account of its _____.

9. A catapult converts _____ energy into _____ energy.

10. Work done is _____ when we hold a pile of books in our hands.

True or False

1. Sound energy cannot be converted into other forms of energy but heat energy can.   (   )

2. Light energy is not as useful as heat energy and potential energy.   (   )

3. Heat energy can travel in a vacuum but sound energy cannot.   (   )

4. A battery has chemicals to convert potential energy to electrical energy. (   )

5. Sound, heat, light, electricity are all forms of energy.   (   )

6. Light energy travels only in straight lines.   (   )

7. MRT trains and cable cars run on electricity.   (   )

8. A wound-up spring and a stretched elastic band possess kinetic energy and can do work.   (   )

9. An electric bulb converts electrical energy into heat energy.   (   )

10. The S.I unit of energy is joule.   (   )

Further Practice

»»» *Write the **correct option** as your answer on the line provided.*

1.   **Which one is the Earth's most important source of energy ?**   _____

(A) Fuel   (B) Sun

(C) Running water   (D) Wind

2.   **Which form of energy causes snow to melt ?**   _____

(A) Heat   (B) Chemical   (C) Kinetic   (D) Electric

3.   **When fuels burn, _____ energy is changed to heat energy.**   _____

(A) kinetic   (B) potential   (C) light   (D) solar

4.   **Street lamps make use of _____ energy produced from _____ energy.**   _____

(A) electrical; potential   (B) electrical; kinetic

(C) solar; electrical   (D) electrical; solar

5.   **Which of the following situations has no work done ?**   _____

(A) A ball falls from a tree due to gravity.

(B) A space ship cruising in space.

(C) A saw cuts a piece of wood.

(D) A boy drags his bag along the floor.

6.   **A hydroelectric power station is built where water is rushing down a river. The moving water has __X__ energy which is used by man to generate__Y__ energy. Which pair of answers fit X and Y most correctly ?**   _____

	X	Y
(A)	Potential	Kinetic
(B)	Electrical	Kinetic
(C)	Kinetic	Electrical
(D)	Sound	Stored

7.   **The dung (waste matter) of cows can be processed and used as a kind of fuel. This fuel is known as**   _____

(A) charcoal.   (B) biogas.   (C) coal.   (D) oil.

8.   **Which of the following statements about energy is not true?**   _____

(A) Energy enables us to do work

(B) Energy cannot be destroyed

(C) Green plants get their energy from the Sun indirectly

(D) Non-living things possess stored energy of their own.

9.   _____ **energy is stored in the water behind a dam on a hill - top.**   _____

(A) Heat   (B) Electrical

(C) Chemical   (D) Gravitational potential

10.   **A rubber ball is held at arm's length above the ground and then dropped. At which point during its fall will its potential energy be equal to its kinetic energy? (You may neglect air resistance and assume that the potential energy is zero at ground level).**   _____

(A) The instant the ball is released.   (B) They are never exactly equal.

(C) At a point halfway down.   (D) Just before the ball touches the ground.

11.   **Raj stretched the elastic rubber band on his catapult and aimed a marble as his target which was a rubber ball. When he released the marble, it hit the ball and the ball fell off the tree stump. Which one of the following best describes the energy transfer and energy changes that took place?**   _____

(A) The kinetic energy from the catapult converted into potential energy and transferred to the ball.

(B) The potential energy from the marble was converted into kinetic energy when it hit the ball.

(C) The kinetic energy from the stretched elastic band was transferred to the marble and the ball.

(D) The potential energy from the stretched elastic band was changed into kinetic energy and transferred from the marble to the ball.

12.   **Study the set-up shown below. Which one of the following correctly describes the conversion of energy that has taken place?**   _____

(A) Light energy $\longrightarrow$ Potential energy

(B) Light energy $\longrightarrow$ Heat energy

(C) Heat energy $\longrightarrow$ Light energy

(D) Light energy $\longrightarrow$ Kinetic energy

Hand lens

Paper

13.   The table below shows the energy conversions of four devices, M, N, O and P?

Devices	Energy conversion
M	Electrical energy → Kinetic energy
N	Potential energy → Kinetic energy
O	Kinetic energy → Sound energy
P	Electrical energy → Heat energy

Which of the following correctly represents the devices in the table?

	M	N	O	P
(A)	Drill	Watch	Telephone	Vacuum Flask
(B)	Vacuum Cleaner	Torchlight	Cooker	Refrigerator
(C)	Toaster	Battery-operated fan	Radio	Solar-cooker
(D)	Escalator	Catapult	Drum	Microwave oven

14.   A pendulum tied to a retort stand is made to swing as shown. At which position does the pendulum bob has the most potential energy ?

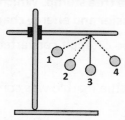

(A) Position 1   (B) Position 4   (C) Position 2   (D) Position 3

15.   A block of ice sliding at a constant speed before moving up a smooth slope is shown. What are the changes in its kinetic energy and gravitational potential energy as it is sliding up the slope ?

	Kinetic Energy	Gravitational potential energy
(A)	Increase	Increase
(B)	Increase	Decrease
(C)	Decrease	Increase
(D)	Decrease	Decrease

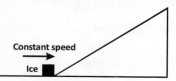

16.   Robin Hood was taking part in an archery contest. When he released
       the arrow shown below, it travelled at a great speed.   _____

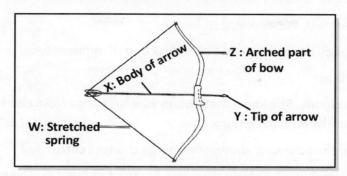

       Which labelled part is responsible for converting potential energy into
       kinetic energy?

       (A) W only   (B) Z only

       (C) W and X only   (D) W, X and Y only

17.   Ram and Ravi pull a table in opposite direction with equal force, then   _____

       (A) work is said to done.   (B) no work is done.

       (C) double work is done.   (D) none of these.

18.   Fandi is playing soccer. At which point does the ball have the least
       potential energy?   _____

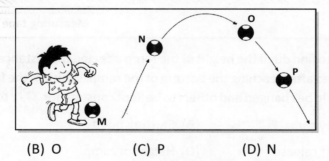

       (A) M   (B) O   (C) P   (D) N

19.   An object moving at constant speed on a frictionless floor has no work
       done because   _____

       (A) there is no resultant force acting on the object.

       (B) there is no distance moved by the object.

       (C) the object has no energy.

       (D) the object has low inertia.

20.   **Work is said to be done when force acts on a body**

(A) but the body does not move.

(B) and moves it in the direction of force.

(C) but the body does not move in the direction of applied force.

(D) none of these

21.   **Jane set up a circuit. She knew that energy had to change from one form to another for the bulb to light up.**

Which one of the following shows the energy changes correctly ?

(A) Electrical energy → Chemical energy → Heat energy → Light energy

(B) Heat energy → Stored energy → Light energy

(C) Chemical energy → Electrical energy → Heat energy → Light energy

(D) Stored energy → Chemical energy → Light energy

22.   **Some pupils set up an experiment shown below.**

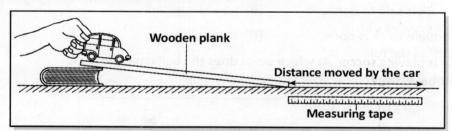

They wanted to find out if the height of the ramp affected the distance that the toy car travelled after reaching the bottom of the ramp. Which of the following variables should be changed and others to be kept constant for a fair test ?

(A) Type of toy car   (B) Starting point

(C) Method of release   (D) Height of ramp

23.   **Mr. Lim is bowling. The rolling ball.**

(A) does not have enough stored energy.

(B) has only kinetic energy.

(C) obtains energy from Mr. Lim's moving hand.

(D) obtains energy from the food that Mr. Lim ate that day.

》》》 Write the **correct options** as your answer on the line provided.

1. **Water is boiling in the kettle. Which form(s) of energy is/are used or produced as the water starts to boil ?** _____

    (A) Heat   (B) Electrical   (C) Sound   (D) Chemical

2. **Fuels can exist as** _____

    (A) gases.   (B) liquids.   (C) solids.   (D) liquid only.

3. **Which of the following does not possess chemical energy ?** _____

    (A) Wound-up toy duck   (B) Used battery

    (C) Charcoal   (D) Stretched rubber band

4. **An electrician is using a power drill to make a hole in the wall. Which form(s) of energy produced is/are not useful ?** _____

    (A) Kinetic   (B) Heat   (C) Sound   (D) None of the above

5. **Which of the following statements about energy is/are true ?** _____

    (A) It can be stored   (B) It exists only in one form

    (C) It enables us to do work   (D) It can be used to exert a force

6. **Which of the following correctly shows the conversions of energy ?** _____

    (A) Computer: Electrical → Sound + Heat + Light

    (B) Telephone: Mechanical → Sound

    (C) Bicycle dynamo: Mechanical → Electrical + Light

    (D) Table lamp: Electrical → Light

7. **A group of children (A, B, C and D) made the following statements about light energy and heat energy. Which of these children made a correct statement?** _____

    (A) The Sun is our main source of heat energy and light energy.

    (B) All sources of heat are also light sources.

    (C) Both light and heat can travel in all directions.

    (D) Dark-coloured objects absorb more heat than light-coloured ones.

8. **Which of the following has potential energy?** _____

    (A) A ball of plasticine   (B) A compressed spring

    (C) A stretched elastic band   (D) A crushed-up sheet of paper

9.   Mahesh rolled a marble on a levelled cement floor. After a while, the marble came to a stop. Which of the following statements correctly explains, why the marble came to a stop ?

(A) The kinetic energy of the marble was changed into heat energy and sound energy.

(B) The kinetic energy in the marble was converted into potential energy.

(C) There was friction between the moving marble and the cement floor.

(D) All the above.

10.   The figure given shows the side view of a tram truck. The car is released from position P. Which of the following statements is/are true ?

(A) The total energy is the same at each of the three positions shown.

(B) The kinetic energy of the car is greater at Q than at R.

(C) The gravitational potential energy of the car is greater at R than at P.

(D) All the above

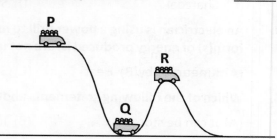

Numerical Problems

1.   A stone that weighs 2 kg is thrown vertically upwards with a kinetic energy of 250 J. How high will the stone go before it returns to the ground? You may assume all the kinetic energy of the stone is changed into potential energy (1kgf - 10N).

2.   A body of mass 1 kg is released at A to move along the path ABC as shown below. Calculate the kinetic energy possessed by the body at B. Assume mechanical energy of the body is conserved. (g = 10 m s^{-2}).

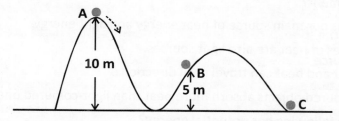

3.   A wooden box of mass 10 kg is carried in a lift from the ground floor to the tenth floor. If the height of each floor is 3 m, what is the work done on the box? (Take acceleration due to gravity, g = 10 m s^{-2}).

4.   Calculate the kinetic energy of a car of mass 1400 kg that is moving at 20 m s⁻¹ along a straight horizontal road.

5.   The velocity of a body of mass 1 kg is increased from 3 m s⁻¹ to 6 m s⁻¹ in some time interval. Calculate the gain in kinetic energy of the body in that time interval.

6.   Two men are exercising in a gym. Sam is 20 years old, 1.60 m tall and has a mass of 75 kg. Tom is 30 years old, 1.65 m tall and has a mass of 60 kg. Both of them take an energy drink that provides 200 KJ of energy. What is the force exerted by each man to move an object a distance of 1 m while using up this energy ?

7.   A boy drops a ball of mass 500 g from a height of 10 m. Ignoring the effect of air resistance, calculate the kinetic energy it possesses at point 3 (i.e., just before it reaches the earth). ($g = 10$ m s⁻²).

8.   A box of mass 2 kg is lifted diagonally from point A to point B as shown. Given that the acceleration due to gravity is 10 m s⁻², what is the gravitational potential energy gained by the box ?

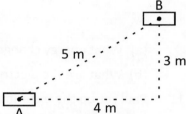

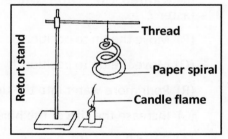

Conceptual Questions

1.   Why is the work done by gravity zero when a girl weighing 300 N jumps and steps on the same place on the ground?

2.   A group of students set up the experiment.

      (a) What happens to the paper spiral ?

      (b) What form of energy is produced by the burning candle ?

      (c) How does the form of energy in (b) cause the observation in (a) ?

3.   A group of immigrants found a vast piece of unoccupied land with coal stored underground. They decided to settle there. There was plenty of sunshine and a river nearby.

      (a) What are the sources of energy that the settlers could make use of ?

      (b) Which source of energy in (a) is renewable ?

4.   What are the two electrical appliances that can make use of energy from the sun ?

5.   In which situation, a man makes use of light energy to warn people of dangers ?

6.   Ravi gives a push to the swing his sister is sitting on. The swing moves away and then returns back to Ravi. The swing repeats this movement several times and finally comes to a stop. What causes the swing to swing up and down and finally stop?

---

7. A box is released from a certain height above a vertical spring located on the ground. After the box touches the spring, it will continue pressing it until the box stops moving. Assuming negligible air friction, what is the energy conversion happening in this event?

8. Why is intake of food an important source of energy in all living beings ?

9. John and Samy were feeling cold. They rubbed their hands vigorously. Why did they do so ? Explain briefly.

10. Study the diagram shown.

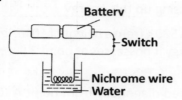

    (a) What energy changes take place in the set-up shown?

    (b) What are the electrical appliances that make use of nichrome wires ?

11. Paul set up the experiment as shown. He drilled a hole at the bottom of a tin. Then he filled the tin with water and fixed it at position 2 on a retort stand. He held a water wheel beneath it.

    Which of the following should Paul do if he wanted the water wheel to spin faster ?

    (P) Move the tin to position 3

    (Q) Move the tin to position 1

    (R) Pour more water into the tin

    (S) Increase the size of the hole.

    (A) P and R   (B) P and S   (C) Q and R   (D) Q and S

> **Brain Nurtures**

1. Four girls wore four different pairs of spring shoes. As they stood on the ground, the springs got compressed by different amounts as indicated by the table given below.

	Michele	Elvi	Ivana	Vania
Compression of the springs (cm)	4	3	2	1

    If all of them jump at the same time, who will most likely jump the highest ?

    (A) Michele   (B) Elvi   (C) Ivana   (D) Vania

2. Four identical lorries M, N, O and P, are driven at the speeds in the ratio of 7 : 2 : 5 : 3 respectively. Arrange the lorries in ascending order of the amount of Kinetic energy they possess.

3. Identify a correct energy conversion that takes place in a television and electric drill.

	Television	Electric drill
(A)	Potential energy, heat energy and sound energy.	Potential energy and sound energy
(B)	Sound energy, heat energy and kinetic energy	Potential energy and kinetic energy
(C)	Light energy, sound energy and heat energy	Kinetic energy and sound energy
(D)	Heat energy, kinetic energy and light energy	Heat energy and kinetic energy

4. Study the illustration of the bouncing ball shown below. Which one of the following graphs correctly shows the energy conversions that occur between M and N ?

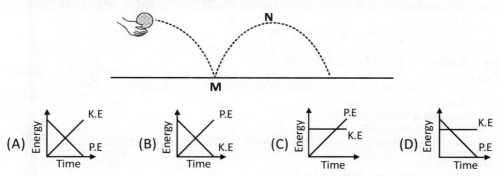

5. The diagram below shows how one form of energy can be converted to another form. P, Q, R and S represent different forms of energy conversions.

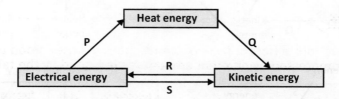

In which of the following does energy conversion represented by arrow R take place?

(A) An electric cooker   (B) An electric drill

(C) A generator producing electricity (D) A battery-operated watch

6. Kim made the toy as shown by using a match box, ice-cream sticks, a rubber band and a plastic roller.

    (a) What should she do to make the match box move on the floor?

    (b) What made the toy move?

7. A car moving to the right has a kinetic energy of 8 joule. A truck, with the same mass, is moving to the left with the same speed. What will be the kinetic energy of the truck?

8. State the energy conversions in the following examples. Make use of arrows (→) to represent 'changes to'.

    (a) When a guitar is strummed (played).

    (b) When a battery-operated fan is switched on.

    (c) When a computer is switched on for playing computer games.

9. Four processes, P, Q, R and S given below involve different energy changes.

    P : Releasing a wound-up toy mouse

    Q : Rubbing a coin on the ground

    R : Running water to move a turbine connected to a dynamo

    S : Burning some firewood

    Which of the following clearly represents the energy conversions that take place in the processes?

(A)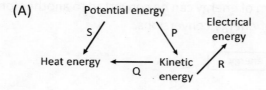

(B)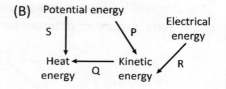

(C)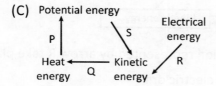

(D)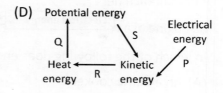

10.   Four blocks, P, Q, R and S having same weight were hung at different heights and four identical nails were placed below each weight on a board as shown below.

(a) All four blocks were then dropped. Which block drives the nail in the board the farthest?

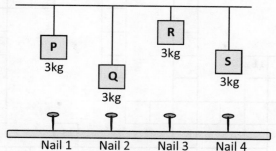

(b) Arrange the nails (1, 2, 3 and 4) in order to how deep into the board each nail was driven. Begin with the nail that was driven the least.

(c) What energy changes took place when the blocks fell on the board ?

Application Based

1)   When a fully inflated balloon is pricked, what form(s) of energy is/are released ?

(A) Sound   (B) Light   (C) Mechanical   (D) Chemical

2)   What energy is converted into sound and kinetic energy of air when a balloon bursts?

(A) Kinetic energy of the pin bursting the balloon

(B) Potential energy of the compressed air inside it

(C) Its gravitational potential energy

(D) Energy is created upon bursting

3)   Solar panels convert _____ energy to _____ energy.

4)   Each floor of an apartment is 5 m above the one below it. A girl of weight 40 kg climbs 4 floors to reach her flat. How many calories does she burn in this process ?

5)   The engine of a vehicle converts _____ energy to _____ energy.

Crossword

ACROSS

1 Friction, the motion of a body.

5 A contact force that opposes the sliding of a body.

8 Ability to do work.

10 With the use of ball bearings friction can be

12 The pull of earth on other objects.

14 The force applied by static charges.

16 A body possesses potential energy by virtue of its

18 Potential energy.

19 A magnet exerts force on a magnetic substance.

20 The SI unit of force.

DOWN

2 Energy of water in dams.

3 Energy that cannot travel in vacuum.

4 Energy possessed by a moving object.

6 This displaces the body and work is said to be done.

7 The most important source of energy on the earth.

9 Energy in a stretched rubber band.

11 A moving body that changes by applied force.

13 SI unit of work or energy.

15 A force that acts on a body directly.

17 The gravitational force acting on an object.

Chapter 7

Heat

Synopsis

Heat

Heat is a form of energy. It can travel through vacuum. The degree of hotness and coldness of a body is called its temperature. When two bodies are in contact, heat energy always flows from the body at higher temperature to the body at lower temperature. When we touch something and find it hot, it is because our body is comparatively colder than it and heat energy flows from the object to our body. Similarly, when we touch a cold object, transfer of heat energy takes place from our body to the object.

There is no net flow of heat energy between two objects at the same temperature. Heat is the energy transferred between two bodies because of the temperature difference between them.

S.I. Unit of Heat is Joule

Sources of heat

The main sources of heat are the sun, electricity and fire. Sun is the natural source of heat energy on our planet. Electricity gives us heat in many different ways. For example, an electric iron can be heated using electricity to press clothes. Similarly, by using electricity, an induction plate produces heat to cook food, a tea or coffee maker provides heat to boil water, a room heater produces heat to warm up the air in a room and so on.

Inflammable substances :

Substances that can catch fire easily are called inflammable substances. Some common examples that catch fire easily are dry paper, leaves, wood, cloth, petrol, kerosene oil, plastics, wax, LPG and hydrogen.

Non-flammable substances:

Substances that do not catch fire easily are called non-flammable substances. Some common examples that do not catch fire easily are metals, stones, alloys, bricks, water and asbestos.

Temperature and its measurement

The measure of the degree of hotness or coldness of a body is called temperature.

* Temperature is generally measured in degree celsius (°C) and degree Fahrenheit (°F). The SI unit of temperature is kelvin (K).

Heat	Temperature
Heat is a form of energy.	Temperature is a measure of the degree of hotness or coldness of a body.
The amount of heat energy is measured in Joule (J).	The degree of hotness or coldness of an object is measured in degree Celsius (°C) or kelvin (K).
Heat flows from a hot region to a cold region.	Temperature of an object increases when heated and decreases when cooled.
Heat can do work	Temperature cannot do work.

》》》 **Effects of Heat**

When heat is supplied to an object, it shows many effects.

Change in temperature

When heat is supplied to an object, there is a rise in the temperature of the object. The rise in temperature depends upon the amount of heat supplied, the mass of the object and the nature of the material of the object. There are a few exceptions to this phenomenon, which you will learn in later classes.

Change in size of the body

The size or volume of substances increases or expands on heating. This increase in the size of a body due to heating is called thermal expansion. Thermal expansion takes place in all bodies and in all states of matter. Similarly, when a substance is cooled, it contracts. There are a few exceptions to this phenomenon, which you will learn in later classes.

Change in state

The change of a substance from one physical state to another is called change of state. The change in the state of a substance is generally caused by a rise or fall in the temperature of the substance.

The following are the processes that are related to the change of state of a substance:

Melting: A solid changes to a liquid state at some fixed temperature by the absorption of heat energy.

Freezing: A liquid changes to solid state at some fixed temperature, by losing heat energy.

Boiling : A liquid changes into gaseous state at some fixed temperature by absorption of heat energy.

Evaporation: The change of a substance from its liquid state to its gaseous state at any temperature below its boiling point.

Condensation: A substance in its vapour or gaseous state changes into its liquid state at some fixed temperature by release of heat energy.

Sublimation: Certain substances change directly from their solid state to their gaseous or vapour state on heating without undergoing the process of melting.

⟫⟫ Conductors

Substances that allow heat energy to flow through them easily are called good conductors of heat. All metals are good conductors of heat. Silver is the best conductor of heat. Some other good conductors are copper, aluminium, gold and iron.

⟫⟫ Insulators

Substances that do not allow heat energy to flow through them easily are called bad conductors of heat or insulators. Glass, mica, cotton, cork, wood, asbestos, plastics and ebonite are some of the bad conductors of heat. All liquids (except mercury) are bad conductors of heat. Air and water are bad conductors of heat.

⟫⟫ Uses of conductors and insulators

Handles of cooking vessels and kettles are made up of insulators such as plastics, so we can hold them easily. Cooking vessels are made up of metals so that they can readily absorb heat and transfer it to the food being cooked. Copper tubes are used in automobile radiators, as copper readily absorbs and conducts away heat from the hot liquid coming from the engine. Cooling coils of copper are used in refrigerators and air conditioners for the same reason. Quilts, blankets and woollen clothes keep us warm in winter because they trap air in between our body and themselves. The trapped air, being a bad conductor, does not allow heat from our body to escape to the surroundings and thus we stay warm.

Ice-boxes are made of double-walled containers. Air is trapped in the space between the two walls. As air is a bad conductor of heat, it does not allow the outside heat to enter the box and the ice does not melt.

Igloos are made from snow. The air trapped in snow acts as an insulator and does not allow heat from inside to go out, thus, keeping the igloo warm. False ceilings, generally made up of Plaster of Paris or asbestos, provide a layer of air between the two ceilings, which keeps the room warm during winter and cool during summer.

Solved Examples

>>> **Example 1 :**

A student found that when he wears a dark coloured shirt and stands outside under the sunlight, he feels hotter and sweats more as shown in figure (a).

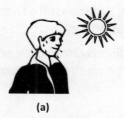 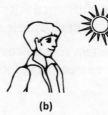

(a)   (b)

(a) Based on the observations in figures (a) and (b).

(i)   What is the difference in the amount of heat received by the student ?

(ii) What inference can be made ?

(iii) What is the effect of colour on heat absorption?

Solution:

(i)   He absorbs more heat wearing the black shirt.

(ii) The colour of the shirt affects the amount of heat absorbed.

(iii) The darker the colour of the shirt, greater the amount of heat absorbed.

>>> **Example 2 :**

The given diagram shows an experiment.

Water is cooled in a beaker and the temperature of the water is recorded every 5 minutes as given below.

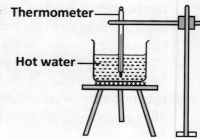

Thermometer

Hot water

Time (minutes)	0	5	10	15	20
Temperature (°C)	80	76	72	68	64

What will be the temperature of the water at 25 minutes, if it is cooled at the same rate ?

Solution:

>>> **Example 3 :**

A cup of hot coffee is placed on a table. What happens to the hot coffee after an hour?

(A)   It will gain heat from the surroundings.

(B)   It will remain at the same temperature.

(C)   It will evaporate.

(D)   It will lose heat to the surroundings.

> **Solution:**

>>> **Example 4 :**

A student carried out an experiment as shown below.

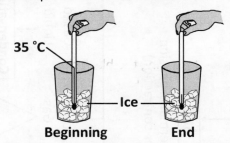

35 °C

Ice

Beginning   **End**

What is the possible temperature reading at the end of the experiment ?

(A) – 10 °C   (B) 0 °C   (C) 37 °C   (D) 100 °C

Solution: (B)

The actual temperature of ice could be zero or less than zero. But a common thermometer has a lowest reading of 0 °C

>>> **Example 5 :**

Substances can change from one state to another upon heating or cooling. Which of the given processes occur by absorbing heat by substances?

(A) Boiling   (B) Sublimation   (C) Melting   (D) All the three

> **Solution:**

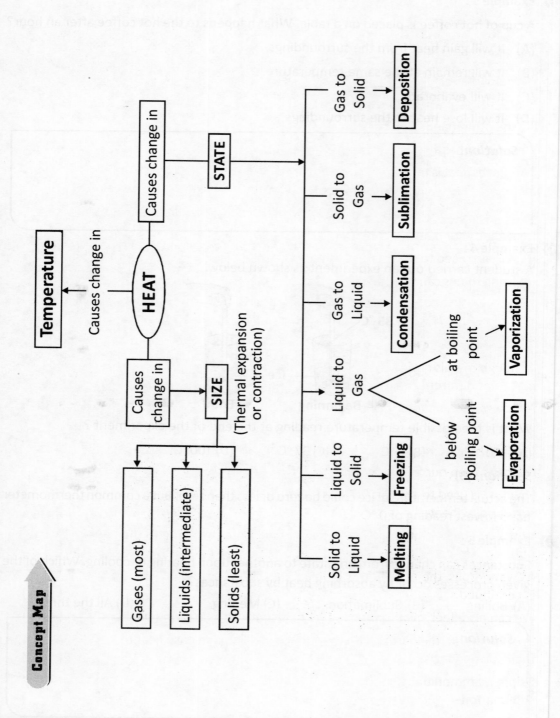

Concept Map

HEAT

Causes change in → Temperature

Causes change in → STATE

Causes change in → SIZE (Thermal expansion or contraction)

SIZE:
- Gases (most)
- Liquids (intermediate)
- Solids (least)

STATE:
- Solid to Liquid → Melting
- Liquid to Solid → Freezing
- Liquid to Gas
  - at boiling point → Vaporization
  - below boiling point → Evaporation
- Gas to Liquid → Condensation
- Solid to Gas → Sublimation
- Gas to Solid → Deposition

> ## Basic Practice

Fill the blanks

1. Heat is a form of _____.

2. If an object gains heat it becomes _____.

3. On the other hand, if an object loses heat it becomes _____.

4. A hot object has a _____.

5. Whenever heat is transferred to an object without changing its state its _____ increases.

6. _____ is constantly transferred from a hotter object to a colder object.

7. Heat keeps our body and our environment _____.

8. Heat is also used to drive steam generators to produce _____.

9. No living things can live without _____.

10. The greater the difference in temperature, the _____ the heat flows.

True or False

1. Although metals are good conductors, heat flows through different metals at different rates. ( )

2. Air is a good conductor of heat. ( )

3. Kettles and hot plates are made from metals that can conduct heat rapidly. ( )

4. When we sleep in sleeping bags in the open air during camping trips, the bags keep our bodies warm. ( )

5. Sawdust is used to cover ice blocks to insulate them from the surrounding heat. ( )

6. When an object is heated, heat is transferred from the flame to the object. ( )

7. As water boils, the temperature remains at 0°C even though heating is continued. ( )

8. We can also 'feel' evaporation if a bit of alcohol is rubbed on our skin. ( )

9. In evaporation, the particles on the surface of a liquid release heat to their surroundings. ( )

10. Sulphur, ammonium chloride and naphthalene can all undergo sublimation. ( )

> **Further Practice**

》》》 *Write the **correct option** as your answer on the line provided.*

1.   **Quantity of heat is measured in**

(A) degrees Celsius.   (B) kelvin.

(C) joules.   (D) amperes.

2.   **The main source of heat for the Earth is the**

(A) sun.   (B) electric current.

(C) combustion of wood.   (D) combustion of fossil fuels.

3.   **In which situation is an insulator of heat not used?**

(A) Ice blocks are covered with sawdust.

(B) The handle of a soldering iron is made up of plastic.

(C) Frying pans are made up of aluminium.

(D) Birds fluff their feathers on a cold day.

4.   **Which of the following processes release heat energy?**

I. Condensation   II. Freezing   III. Melting   IV. Boiling

(A) I and II only   (B) I and III only   (C) II and IV only   (D) III and IV only

5.   **Iodine crystals are mixed with some sand. Which process will enable you to obtain pure iodine?**

(A) Freezing   (B) Melting   (C) Condensation   (D) Sublimation

6.   **Which of the following occurs when water first reaches its boiling point?**

(A) It loses heat and its temperature remains constant.

(B) It gains heat and its temperature remains constant.

(C) It loses heat and its temperature drops.

(D) It gains heat and its temperature increases.

7.   **Which quantity must be the same for two bodies if they are said to be in thermal equilibrium?**

(A) Density   (B) Potential energy

(C) Temperature   (D) Mass

8.   **Cooking utensils are always fitted with plastic handles as they are**

(A) good thermal conductors.   (B) not strong.

(C) poor thermal conductors.   (D) denser.

9. Given below are some materials grouped as M and N respectively. Which material can be placed in group "N"?

    Group M - Copper, Aluminium   Group N - Glass, Sand

    (A) Stainless steel   (B) Paper

    (C) Zinc   (D) Iron

10. A boy took a canned drink out of the refrigerator and placed it on the table. He saw droplets of water on the surface of the can and after sometime they disappeared. Which of the following processes explain his observations?

    (A) Melting, followed by condensation

    (B) Freezing, followed by condensation

    (C) Evaporation, followed by condensation

    (D) Condensation, followed by evaporation

11. An equal amount of hot soup is poured into four similar-sized bowls made up of different materials and left to cool for 10 minutes. In which bowl will the soup be the hottest?

    (A) Aluminium   (B) Copper   (C) Plastic   (D) Polystyrene

12. Which of the following processes requires heat to flow from the substance to the surroundings?

    (A) Boiling   (B) Melting   (C) Evaporation (D) Condensation

13. Which of the following is not a source of heat?

    (A) Sound   (B) The Sun   (C) Electricity   (D) Burning fuels

14. Which of the following statements about heat is true?

    (A) It can be seen.   (B) It is a form of matter.

    (C) It is not as useful as light.   (D) It keeps living things warm.

15. Which statement about poor conductors of heat is true?

    (A) Heat can pass through them easily.

    (B) Poor conductors are always hot.

    (C) Heat cannot pass through them easily.

    (D) Poor conductors are more expensive than good conductors.

16. Heat gain can cause matter to change from

    (A) gas to liquid or liquid to solid. (B) solid to liquid or liquid to gas.

    (C) gas to liquid or solid to liquid. (D) solid to liquid or gas to liquid.

17. X is taken in by a solid to change into a liquid and also liquid to gas. X is also given off when it changes from gas to liquid and also liquid to solid. What can X be?

(A) Carbon dioxide (B) Oxygen (C) Light (D) Heat

18. The diagram given below shows a copper wire that has been placed in two basins of water. The arrow indicates how heat travels through the copper wire.

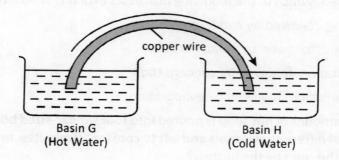

copper wire

Basin G
(Hot Water)

Basin H
(Cold Water)

What conclusion can you draw from the given information?

(A) The water in basin G has a higher temperature than the water in basin H.

(B) The copper wire is a bad conductor of heat and electricity.

(C) Water has a fixed volume but has no fixed shape.

(D) Heat is a form of energy, not matter.

19. What happens when ice cubes in a container are melting?

(A) The ice cubes release heat.

(B) The ice cubes absorb heat.

(C) The ice cubes change into the gaseous state.

(D) The temperature of the ice cubes rises to room temperature.

20. A girl rubbed her two hands against each other. After a while, both the hands became warm. What does this prove ?

(A) Our body loses heat.

(B) Heat gain causes matter to expand.

(C) Rubbing produces heat.

(D) She has fever.

>>>> Write the **correct options** as your answer on the line provided.

1. **Which of the following activities will produce heat?** _____

(A) Bending a paper clip back and forth repeatedly.

(B) Rubbing hands together.

(C) Hitting a piece of metal with a hammer.

(D) Striking a nail into a wall.

2. **Which of the following are done to prevent heat loss?** _____

(A) Ice blocks are covered with saw dust.

(B) Birds fluff up their feathers.

(C) Hot food is wrapped in aluminium foil.

(D) Stirring hot milk to dissolve sugar.

3. **A student set up the following to compare the rate at which ice melted when placed in water at different temperatures.** _____

Water at 30°C with one ice cube   Water at 30°C with two ice cubes   Water at 10°C with one ice cube   Water at 10°C with two ice cubes

What must be changed in her experiment to make it a fair test?

(A) All the glasses should have the same number of ice cubes.

(B) The temperature of water in all the glasses should be the same.

(C) The temperature of water in all the glasses should be different.

(D) All the glasses should have water with a temperature higher than room temperature.

4. **A metal cube is heated over a flame for 10 minutes. What is likely to happen to the metal cube ?** _____

(A) An increase in volume.   (B) An increase in temperature.

(C) An increase in mass.   (C) An increase in weight.

5. **The amount of heat an object can receive from another object at a fixed temperature depends on the** _____

(A) type of material.   (B) temperature.

(C) mass of the object.   (D) contraction.

6.   **Heat is used to do certain activities like**   _____

(A) cooking food and boiling water.   (B) ironing our clothes.

(C) drying our clothes and foods.   (D) providing hot water for bathing.

7.   **Which of the following are poor conductors of heat ?**   _____

(A) Air   (B) Steel   (C) Wood   (D) Plastic

8.   **What happens when a 80 °C metal piece is placed in a room having temperature of 25 °C ?**   _____

(A) After a while, the temperature of the metal will decrease.

(B) The heat is released from the metal.

(C) The room will heat up to 80 °C after long time.

(D) The room will cool to 10 °C.

9.   **Identify a use of heat in our daily life.**   _____

(A) It is used to cook food.   (B) It maintains our body temperature.

(C) It is absorbed by ice to melt.   (D) It is used to sterilise medical equipment.

10.   **A block of ice is left on a table top at room temperature. What will happen to the block of ice?**   _____

(A) It will melt and cause a change in shape.

(B) It will gain heat and change to another state of matter.

(C) It will gain heat and change to other substances.

(D) Its temperature will increase to room temperature before it melts.

Conceptual Questions

1.   State the difference between heat and temperature.

2.   A coin is cold when you touch it in the morning. Give a reason for this.

3.   Metals are used to make various cooking utensils such as stainless steel kettles and copper-based frying pans.

(a) Why is metal used to make cooking utensils?

(b) What is the advantage of using copper-based frying pans?

4.   What is the main reason for using polystyrene to make boxes for packing takeaway food and boxes for storing cold items?

5.   Why does a liquid expand more than a solid when heated by the same temperature difference ?

6.   What is wrong with the statement "body a higher temperature contains more heat"?

7.　　Compare boiling and evaporation

　　　(a)　when the temperature change occurs.

　　　(b)　where the change occurs.

　　　(c)　rate of change.

8.　　Stainless steel cooking pans are preferred with extra copper bottom. Why ?

9.　　A piece of paper wrapped tightly on a wooden piece is found to get charred quickly when held over a flame, compared to a similar piece of paper when wrapped on a brass rod. Explain why?

10.　　In terms of thermal expansion, why is it important that a key and its lock be made of the same or similar materials?

Brain Nurtures

1.　　Water is slowly heated from room temperature to 50 °C. Why the volume of water decreases slowly during the heating?

2.　　When water gains heat, it changes into water vapour. 20 cm^3 of water forms more than 20 000 cm^3 of water vapour but the amount of particles (matter) in water remains the same. What do you understand from this change?

3.　　Three bottles were filled with the same amount of substances, X, Y and Z, respectively. The bottles were placed in a basin of hot water of 80 °C at the same time. After 2 minutes, the bottles were removed from the basin of water and left in an air-conditioned room of temperature 20 °C.

　　　The temperatures of the substances that were taken every two minutes are given below.

Time (min)	Temperature (°C)		
	Substance X	Substance Y	Substance Z
0	43	64	50
2	42	58	48
4	41	52	46
6	40	46	44
8	39	40	42
10	38	34	40

　　　What happened to the temperatures of the three substances after the bottles were removed from the hot water and left in an air-conditioned room?

4.　　What happens when a beaker of hot water at 70 °C is left in a room that has a temperature of 25 °C.?

5.   There is a slight temperature difference between the waterfall at the top and bottom, why?

6.   Can water in a beaker be made to boil by placing it in a bath of boiling water?

7.   Three containers of water were set up as shown below. Which beaker has the most heat energy compared to itself when it is at 0 °C?

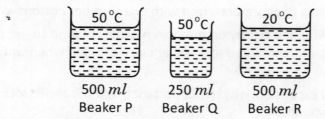

8.   Can water be made to boil without heating?

9.   After you measure the dimensions of a plot of land with a steel tape on a hot day, you return and remeasure the same plot on a cold day. On which day do you determine the larger area for the land?

10.   Why are incandescent bulbs typically made of very thin glass?

Application Based

1)   Golu connected his mobile to a charger and after sometime observed that his mobile was warmer than when he had put it for charging. Why did his mobile become warmer than before although there was no apparent source of heat around it ?

2)   Which of the following converts heat energy to electrical energy ?

      (A) Turbine   (B) Thermal power plant

      (C) Solar panel   (D) An electric heater

3)   1 MJ = _____ kJ ?

4)   After driving a vehicle for sometime, we observe that its tyres will be hotter than the surrounding temperature. What causes this heating of the tyres ?

      (A) It is heat gained from the hot roads

      (B) Heat from the engine flows to the tyres

      (C) Sunlight falling on the tyres makes them hot

      (D) Friction between the tyres and the road causes the tyres to heat up.

5)   Mercury thermometer works on the principle of

      (A) thermal expansion.   (B) gravity.

      (C) glass reacting with mercury.   (D) none of these

Chapter 8

Sound

Synopsis

>>>> **Sound**

Sound is a form of energy produced by vibrating bodies. When particles or objects vibrate, they transfer the energy to the molecules of the surrounding medium (e.g., air) The molecules that receive this energy begin to vibrate and in turn, pass this energy to the adjacent molecules. These vibrations that travel in the form of waves in all directions are called sound waves. When sound waves reach our ears, they cause a sensation that is further carried by nerves to the brain.

Sources of sound

Any object that vibrates mechanically produces a sound, that may be or may not be heard by us. Sources of sound are innumerable but a few are tuning fork, toothed wheel, bell, siren etc.

Sound - a medium to travel

Sound can travel through all states of matter like solids, liquids and gases. But it cannot travel through vacuum due to the absence of molecules to transfer and pass on the energy to the molecules in the surroundings.

Speed of sound

Speed of sound is not the same in all states of matter. The speed of sound depends on the density of the medium. The density of solids is the maximum, followed by the density of liquids and gases. Sound travels the fastest through solids, little slower through liquids and slowest through gases or air. The speed of sound also depends upon the pressure and speed of the fluid medium, temperature and humidity (in case of a gaseous medium).

Compressions and rarefactions - Tuning fork

A vibrating body moves to-and-fro about its mean position. When the vibrating body moves outwards, it increases pressure on the molecules of the medium surrounding it

---

(e.g. air) and causes them to come close to each other. This is known as compression. When the vibrating body moves inwards, the pressure on the molecules gets reduced. So, the gaps between the molecules increase causing them to spread out. This is known as rarefaction.

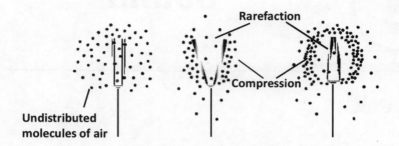

Thus, a series of compressions and rarefactions move away from the vibrating body, causing a sound wave, much like a ripple in water.

Reflection of sound

Sound energy, like light energy, obeys the laws of reflection.

1. Its angle of incidence is equal to angle of reflection.

2. Incident wave, reflected wave and the normal wave lie in the same plane.

    The figure shown below represents the laws of reflection of sound waves.

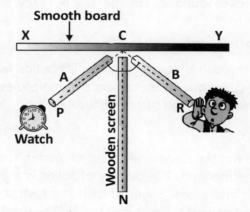

Echo

An echo is a repetition of sound produced by the reflection of sound waves from a reflecting surface. Our brain retains the effect of every sound for 1/10 of a second and so it cannot distinguish between two different sounds if they reach the brain within a duration of 1/10 of a second (0.1 sec). This characteristic property of human hearing is known as persistence of hearing. In order to be heard as two distinct sounds, the two sound signals must reach the brain at a time interval of more than 1/10 of a second.

As in a large hall, sound gets reflected in a small room, too. However, in a small room, the distance between the walls is small. So, the two sounds (original and reflected) reach us in less than 1/10 of a second. That is why, in a small room, we hear the original sound and the reflected sound at the same time. So, there is no echo.

Minimum distance required for occurrence of an echo

We know that the speed of sound in air is 332 m/s and the minimum time required to hear an echo is 0.1 s.

So, the distance travelled by sound in 0.1 s = 332 × 0.1 m = 33.2 m.

As the sound travels twice between the source and the reflecting surface before an echo is heard, the minimum distance required to hear an echo = $\dfrac{33.2}{2}$ m = 16.6 m.

Audibility - Audible and inaudible sounds

The range of frequencies that the listener can distinguish is known as the range of audibility. The top and bottom of this range are known as the limits of audibility. The lower limit is supposed to be 20 Hz and the upper limit is above 20 000 Hz. If a long strip of metal is set into vibration, it can be seen vibrating but no sound can be heard. This is because the sound is below the lower limit of audibility.

Human beings can hear sounds of frequencies between 20 Hz and 20,000 Hz. This is called the audible range. Vibrations below 20 Hz and above 20,000 Hz are not audible to humans. So, sounds that have frequencies between 20 Hz and 20,000 Hz are also known as sonic sounds. Vibrations below 20 Hz are called infrasonic sounds and those above 20 000 Hz are called ultrasonic sounds (ultrasound).

>>> Characteristics of sound

Each sound we hear is a unique combination of three characteristics that are loudness (or intensity), pitch and quality (or timbre).

Loudness or intensity of sound

Loudness is a characteristic of sound that distinguishes a feeble sound from a loud one of the same frequency.

Pitch

The characteristic of sound that differentiates a shrill sound from a hoarse sound is called pitch.

Quality of sound or timbre

The quality of sound or timbre distinguishes two notes of the same pitch (or frequency) and loudness (or amplitude) produced by different bodies.

Measuring the speed of sound

A direct determination of the speed of sound requires only two measurements: the distance of the source from the observer and the time taken for the sound to travel that distance. Then the speed can be calculated from speed = distance/ time.

Echo method

When a short sharp sound, e.g., clap, is made, it may be reflected by a large obstacle. e.g., a wall and heard by the observer. This reflected pulse is known as an echo. Suppose a person stands 50 m in front of a wall and gives a single clap. When the echo is heard the sound has travelled 100 m. Timing this interval with a stopwatch is not very accurate. However, if a second person holds the stopwatch and the first person claps every time an echo is heard, then the time for a large number of echoes can be obtained with reasonable accuracy.

Suppose the distance of the clapper from the wall is 50 m and the time interval between the first and the one-hundred and first clap is 30 seconds, then

$$\text{Speed of sound} = \frac{\text{Distance travelled}}{\text{Time taken by one clap}} = 100 \text{ m} \div \frac{30}{100} \text{ s} = 333 \text{ m s}^{-1}$$

Variation in the speed of sound

The speed of sound is greater in solids than in liquids, and greater in liquids than in gases. The speed of sound in water is much greater than in air. In fresh water the speed of sound is 1410 m s^{-1}, in sea water it is 1540 m s^{-1}. In iron, the speed of sound is about 5000 m s^{-1}.

By sending out signals and noting the time interval before the reflected signal (echo) arrives, sound pulses are used to determine the depth of the sea, and to locate the position of shoals of fish. During the war, echo sounding with high-frequency sound waves was used to detect the position of enemies.

Atmospheric conditions affect the speed of sound in air. The speed of sound is proportional to the square root of (pressure/density). Changes in pressure do not affect the speed of sound in air. This is because an increase in pressure causes a corresponding increase in density and the ratio of pressure/density remains constant. Changes in temperature do affect the speed of sound in air (or indeed in any gas).

Changes in humidity affect the speed of sound. The density of water vapour is less than the density of dry air at the same pressure. At night, when the humidity tends to rise, sounds travel faster. Sounds can be heard more clearly on a quiet misty night. This is partly because of the increased humidity and partly because under such conditions there is usually a temperature inversion which tends to refract the sounds so that they do not escape.

Solved Examples

》》》 **Example 1 :**

A gun was fired and an observer 900 m away measured the time interval between seeing the flash of the gun and hearing the shot. The duration indicated by a stopwatch is 2.5 s. What is the speed of sound in air ?

Solution:

Distance travelled = 900 m

Time taken = 2.5 s

$$\text{Speed of sound} = \frac{\text{Distance travelled}}{\text{Time taken}} = \frac{900 \text{ m}}{2.5 \text{ s}} = 360 \text{ m s}^{-1}$$

》》》 **Example 2 :**

Sound travels at 343 m/s through air. How far will sound travel in 5 s ?

Solution:

In 1 second sound travels 343 m is air

In 5 second sound travels 343 × 5 = 1715 m.

Sound travels 1715 m in 5 seconds in air.

》》》 **Example 3 :**

The speed of sound in steel is 5,200 m/s. How far will sound travel in 5s through steel?

Solution:

>>> **Example 4 :**

A boy stands in between two cliffs x and y, such that he is at a distance of 66 m from x. When he blows a whistle he hears first echo after 0.4 s and second echo after 1.2 s. Calculate : (i) speed of sound, (ii) distance of cliff y from the boy.

Solution:

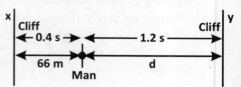

(i) Speed of sound $v = \dfrac{2d}{t} = \dfrac{2 \times 66}{0.4} = 330 \, \text{m s}^{-1}$.

(ii) Distance of man from cliff $y = d = \dfrac{v \times t}{2} = 330 \times \dfrac{1.2}{2} = 198$ m.

>>> **Example 5 :**

The speed of sound at 15 °C is 329 m s^{-1}. Calculate the temperature when the speed of sound is 296 m s^{-1}

Solution:

Initial temperature = 15 °C

Decrease in the speed of sound = (329 − 296) = 33 m s^{-1}

For 0.6 m s^{-1} decrease in speed of sound, fall in temperature = 1 °C.

∴ For 33 m s^{-1} decrease in speed of sound, fall in temperature = $\dfrac{33}{0.6}$ = 55 °C

∴ Final temperature = (15 − 55) °C = 40 °C

>>> **Example 6 :**

The speed of sound at 15 °C is 329 m s^{-1}. Calculate the temperature when the speed of sound is 315 m s^{-1}.

Solution:

Concept Map

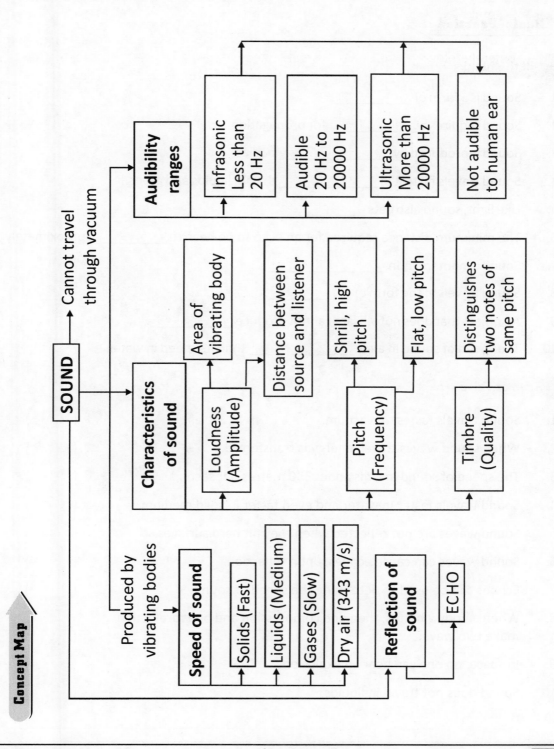

Basic Practice

Fill the blanks

1. Sound is a form of _____.

2. Sound requires a _____ for propagation.

3. Sound is produced by _____ bodies.

4. Sound travels fastest in _____ than in liquids and gases.

5. Like light, sound also gets _____.

6. The minimum distance required for an echo to be heard is _____ approximately.

7. Sound cannot travel in _____.

8. Sound travels in the form of _____.

9. An object that does not vibrate cannot produce _____.

10. The speed of sound in air is _____ than its speed in water.

True or False

1. Sound travels fastest in vacuum.   (   )

2. When sound waves travel, energy is transferred.   (   )

3. The speed of sound in air is about 330 metres per second.   (   )

4. Sound travels faster in water and even faster in solid medium.   (   )

5. Sound waves are not reflected when they hit hard surfaces.   (   )

6. Sound waves can cause echoes, upon reflection.   (   )

7. Echoes can be used to determine the speed of sound.   (   )

8. When a body vibrates, then one compression and one rarefaction make two waves.   (   )

9. In space, no one can hear an explosion.   (   )

10. Sound does not travel in liquids.   (   )

> **Further Practice**

》》》 *Write the **correct option** as your answer on the line provided.*

1.   **Objects produce sound by**

(A) expanding.   (B) heating.   (C) vibrating.   (D) cooling.   _____

2.   **Which of these is true about the speed of sound as it travels through solids, liquids and gases?**   _____

	Solids	Liquids	Gases
(A)	Slowest	Medium speed	Fastest
(B)	Same speed	Same speed	Same speed
(C)	Fastest	Medium speed	Slowest
(D)	Medium speed	Slowest	Fastest

3.   **Why we cannot see sound travelling in the air ?**   _____

(A) It travels too fast

(B) It is a colourless form of energy

(C) It is like infrared or ultraviolet light

(D) Air molecules are very small

4.   **The reason sound travels faster in solids than in liquids because**   _____

(A) the particles of matter are closer in a solid than in a liquid.

(B) there is less friction passing through a solid.

(C) the energy of the particles in solids is greater.

(D) solids have greater space inside for the sound to pass through quicker.

5.   **Which of these statements about sound is true?**   _____

(A) It is a type of radiation.

(B) It is an invisible form of energy.

(C) It is noise expanding outwards.

(D) It is the low energy part of the light spectrum.

6.   **A person speaking through a long tube can be heard much more clearly by another person with his ear to the other end of the tube. This is because sound waves**   _____

(A) are reflected off the walls of the tube.

(B) travel faster when enclosed.

(C) are amplified in the tube.

(D) slow down when enclosed and become louder.

7. **Which of the following explains why you see the flash of an explosion before you hear the boom?**

    (A) Light is a more intense form of energy than sound.

    (B) Light can travel in vacuum but sound cannot.

    (C) Sound is heavier than light.

    (D) Light travels faster than sound.

8. **Which device uses sound (audio) more than video?**

    (A) Laptop computer　　　　　　(B) iPod

    (C) Computer tablet　　　　　　(D) Desktop computer

9. **Which option represents the correct speed of sound in all the three materials below?**

	Soil	Air	Seawater
(A)	1500 m/s	3000 ms/	1800 m/s
(B)	330 m/s	1500 m/s	1800 m/s
(C)	180 m/s	330 m/s	150 m/s
(D)	1800 m/s	330 m/s	1500 m/s

10. **Why is a boy placing his ear to the railing able to hear two sounds when a girl taps once on the railing?**

    (A) The sound wave is refracted through the railing creating two sounds.

    (B) The sound travels through the air and also through the railing.

    (C) The sound itself and also the echo that it produces inside the railing.

    (D) The sound wave is reflected off the ground creating two sounds.

11. **In which of these materials would sound travel the fastest ?**

    (A) Oxygen　　　(B) Lead　　　　(C) Sea water　　　(D) Plastic foam

12. **When compared with the speed of light, the speed of sound is**

    (A) ten times faster.　　　　　　(B) a thousand times faster.

    (C) ten thousand times faster.　　(D) a million times slower.

13. **The velocity of sound in air is nearly**

    (A) 332 m/s.　　(B) 332 mile/s.　(C) 332 ft/s.　　(D) 3.32 km/s.

14. **Sound travels with maximum velocity in**

    (A) gases.　　　(B) liquids.　　　(C) solids.　　　(D) vacuum.

15.   **The velocity of sound in air is not affected by changes in** _____

(A) moisture contents of the air.   (B) the temperature of the air.

(C) the atmospheric pressure.   (D) the composition of air.

16.   **The bells of a college or temple are made of large size to produce** _____

(A) sound of high-pitch.   (B) loud sound.

(C) sound of high quality.   (D) feeble sound.

17.   **Which of the following statements is not true ?** _____

(A) Changes in air temperature have no effect on the speed of sound.

(B) Changes in air pressure have no effect on the speed of sound.

(C) The speed of sound in water is higher than in air.

(D) The speed of light in water is lesser than in air.

18.   **Speed of sound** _____

(A) decreases when we go from solid to gaseous state.

(B) increases with increase in temperature.

(C) depends upon properties of the medium through which it travels.

(D) all these statements are correct.

19.   **Sound can be characterized by its** _____

(A) frequency only.   (B) amplitude only.

(C) speed only.   (D) frequency, amplitude and speed

20.   **Sound is a** _____

(A) mechanical wave.   (B) electro-magnetic wave.

(C) longitudinal waves.   (D) Both (A) and (C)

》》》 *Write the **correct options** as your answer on the line provided.*

1.   **Two student's P and Q have identical drums and sticks. Same number of pieces of paper were placed on both the drums. On beating with sticks, the pieces of paper on student 'Q's drum jumped higher than that of student 'P'. What do you conclude from this activity?** _____

(A) Student P's drum has no sound energy.

(B) Student Q's drum has more sound energy than student P.

(C) One of the drums is making a louder sound than the other.

(D) Both the drums on striking produce feeble sounds.

2.   **Sound will pass through**

      (A) a thick steel door.   (B) a concrete wall.

      (C) thick mud.   (D) vacuum.

3.   **Speed of sound in air depends on**

      (A) humidity.   (B) wind.

      (C) temperature.   (D) none of the above.

4.   **What is necessary for the transmission of sound ?**

      (A) A source   (B) A medium

      (C) A receiver   (D) An absorber

5.   **Which of the following is always true for sound waves?**

      (A) They are produced by vibration

      (B) They are longitudinal waves

      (C) They have an approximate speed of 300 m s^{-1}

      (D) They do not require a medium

6.   **Which of the given frequencies can be heard by a normal human being?**

      (A) 100 Hz   (B) 10000 Hz   (C) 1 Hz   (D) 12 Hz

Numerical Problems

1.   A person claps 20 times in one second while standing in front of a cliff. If the distance between vertical cliff and the person is 880 cm then the sound of clapping and the echo coincides. Determine the velocity of sound.

      Solution:

2.   Police is at P, 200 m from a wall. Thief 'T' is 40 m from police. P fires at T and misses. Thief hears the sound of the gun twice with an interval of one second. Calculate the velocity of sound in air.

Solution:

<hr>

Conceptual Questions

1.   Explain why sound travels faster in solids than liquids and travels the slowest through gases like air.

2.   "We cannot hear the explosions on other planets." Why ?

Solution:

3.   Do compressions and rarefactions in a sound wave travel in the same direction or in opposite directions from one another ?

4.   Why does sound travel faster in warm air ?

5.   What kind of wind conditions will make sound more easily heard at long distances? Less easily heard at long distances ?

> **Brain Nurtures**

1. How will you determine the speed of sound in the air using the echo method? What precautions must be taken to get an accurate result or obtain an approximate value ?

2. If you are near the seashore and there is an explosion at the sea, you will hear two explosions. why ?

3. A person is standing next to a steel railing that is 7,700 m long. His friend is at the other end of the railing and he hits the railing with a hammer. How long will it take for the sound to reach him through the railing ?

   Solution:

4. If the handle of tuning fork is held solidly against a table, the sound from the tuning fork becomes louder. Why ? How will this affect the length of time the fork keeps vibrating? Explain.

5. An experiment was carried out to determine the speed of sound in the laboratory. Two microphones P and Q were placed 0.8 m apart. Each microphone was connected to a sound-operated switch. Microphone P started the electronic timer and microphone Q stopped the timer. When the balloon burst, the electronic timer recorded a time of 2.5 milli seconds. Calculate the speed of sound.

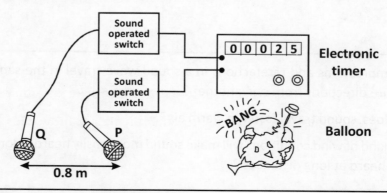

Application Based

1) When a mosquito flies near our ears, we hear an annoying sound. This sound is produced by

(A) flapping of wings of the mosquito.

(B) humming by the mosquito.

(C) our ears make that noise when a mosquito approaches.

(D) none of the above.

2) When we turn up or turn down the volume on a TV or speaker, which characteristic of sound changes ?

(A) Frequency   (B) Intensity   (C) Timbre   (D) All the three

3) As shown below, there are 2 media between a sound source and an observer, one being air and the other being steel, in the form of a bent steel frame.

The straight distance between the sound source and the observer is 50 m. What must be the total length of the steel frame such that sound takes the same time to reach the observer through both the media ? (speed of sound in air = 330 m/s and in steel = 5940 m/s)

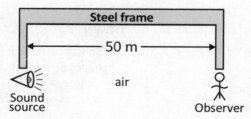

4) Golu was wondering why sound travelled faster in some media than other. He wanted to start with the basics. He learnt that sound travels in the form of compressions and rarefactions.

i) Consider 2 media: steel and air. Which is easier to compress ?

ii) As air is easier to compress than steel, it must be easier to form compressions and rarefactions in air than in steel. Why does sound travel faster in steel than in air ?

5) Suppose two people are talking to each other on phones. How does the voice of one person reach the other ?

Crossword

ACROSS

1 A medium essential for propagation of sound.
3 Other name of frequency.
7 Sound travels in all states of matter except.
8 It occurs in all bodies and all states of matter.
10 It travels from hot place to cool place.
11 Sound also obeys law of.
12 Vibrating objects produce.
14 Substances that allow heat to pass through them.
17 Change of state of a solid to gas on heating.
19 A source of sound in a laboratory.

DOWN

2 Sensation of sound heard by humans.
4 Degree of hotness or coldness of a body.
5 A process that occurs all the time irrespective of temperature in water bodies.
6 A repetition of sound.
8 Change caused due to heating a substance.
9 A natural insulator above the earth's surface.
13 Two notes of same pitch can be determined.
15 The main source of heat on the earth.
16 Speed of sound in solids.
18 The melting point of ice is degrees celcius.